BIBLE STORIES
FOR
YOUNG READERS

Bible Stories

for

Young Readers

ADAPTED BY

April Oursler Armstrong

FROM

"THE GREATEST STORY EVER TOLD"

AND

"THE GREATEST BOOK EVER WRITTEN"

BY

FULTON OURSLER

ILLUSTRATED BY JULES GOTLIEB

JUNIOR DELUXE EDITIONS   GARDEN CITY, N.Y.

FOR MY DAUGHTER, CATHERINE GRACE

CONTENTS

Stories from
the Old Testament

CONTENTS

Stories from
the New Testament

STORIES
FROM
THE OLD TESTAMENT

The Forbidden Tree

Adam opened his eyes and looked into the face of God. God smiled at him, and they were friends, the Lord and the first man He made.

Adam stood up, tall and straight and naked and new, his feet in the red earth from which God made him. He could feel his own heart beating, feel the strength in his own arms and legs. When he breathed, the smell of the woods and flowers was fresh. The wind played in his reddish hair, and cooled his bare skin. How wonderful, how tremendous it was to be alive!

Adam looked at God, and his soul swelled with love and thanksgiving. Adam knelt, and adored God, and the feeling of being close to Him was sweeter and happier than he could bear.

Then God took Adam and showed him the world that was his, the shining, rustling, sunny-shady Garden of Eden, the perfect place, called Paradise. It was to belong to Adam, and to all men after him. Adam was to take care of it, to till the soil and make new things grow, and to live in it. It was a gift from God to man.

A different world from ours that Garden was, more beautiful than any man since Adam has ever seen. Every corner of it was perfect, as God meant it to be. Each plant was perfect, not twisted or scraggly or stunted. Each animal was perfect, none too thin, none crippled, none forlorn. Ugliness had no place in that strong and gentle world. And danger was a stranger there.

Adam was different too. This man who walked with God through the Garden was not like any man in the world today. God's own hands had made him, and so Adam's body was perfect, with not a crooked place or a mark on it, nothing too big or too small. Each muscle was strong and each sense perfect. He could hear even the highest notes of the birds, and the whisper grass makes as it grows.

Adam understood everything in the world immediately. He did not need to study, or to learn by experience. God gave him an understanding of the laws of the heavens and of the earth. And Adam did not need ever be afraid. The animals obeyed him; the weather was kind. There was no sickness. And with the way that God made him, and the extra gifts God gave him, Adam need never grow old. He need never die.

And, most wonderful of all, Adam could see God, and talk with Him, as a son can see and talk with his father. The world was his, and he was God's.

Over the mountains and through the meadows Adam walked with God, marveling at the wonders of Paradise.

Then God said:

"All this is yours, to have and enjoy as you please. I give you but one law, to remind you that I am the Lord and Maker of all.

"You may eat the fruit of every tree in Paradise, except one.

You shall not eat of the fruit of the Tree of Knowledge of Good and Evil. The day that you eat of that tree, you shall die the death."

God's voice was stern. Adam looked carefully at the Tree of Knowledge of Good and Evil and its scarlet fruit. It was a fine tree, but there were thousands of other trees in the Garden—fig trees, nut trees, pears and apples, forest upon forest of trees. And Adam thought:

"What a small thing for God to ask! The least I can do is obey the one rule the Lord gives me. It won't be hard." And Adam smiled, and promised.

Then God left Adam alone to explore the Garden. Adam laughed aloud to see the wind chase the shadows of the leaves. He found cool caves in the hillsides, and ate of the berries that grew in the sun. Birds showed him their nests, and spiders their webs, and rabbits scuttered around his feet, tickling his heels.

He dove into a deep green forest stream, and swam under a tiny waterfall with the gleaming fishes. Then he climbed onto the sun-warmed ferns of the bank to rest. Below him lay a pool of quiet water, smooth as a mirror, and, leaning over, he saw himself for the first time. He looked and looked.

And suddenly Adam was lonely.

He wanted someone like himself, to share this world that God had made. That was the first thing man ever wanted, someone to be with, and to love, to share his life.

God knew. And, watching him, God said: "It is not good for man to be alone."

God led Adam to a tall green hill, and sat him on a white rock. Then from every corner of the Garden God called the other creatures He had made, most of which Adam had not yet seen. From their holes and dens and nests they came, waddling, crawling, hopping, flying, wiggling, running, and leaping.

"Give to each one a name, Adam, and what you call them their names will be. And you are ruler over them all."

Adam (whose own name, which God gave him, meant "man" and was close to the word for "ground," from which he was made) grinned. It was the strangest naming-party ever. One by one he named them: the creeping caterpillar, the willow-necked giraffe, the elephant with his trunk held high, the peacock and the woodpecker, the gnu and the yak and the lion and the cow, the lightning bug and the mosquito, the lizard and the eagle and the frog.

But as Adam saw each one, he grew lonelier and lonelier. Even the ants had other ants to be with. And he had no one.

God knew. He sent the animals away and He looked into Adam's eyes, and suddenly, not knowing why, Adam grew weak, and dizzy. Adam sank into the cool grass, and his eyes blinked and closed. He did not move. He hardly breathed. And in that sleep he could feel nothing.

Sunset crept across the sky. God's hands touched Adam, and reached into his side, and from inside him, with no pain and no blood, God took one rib bone. The hole in Adam's side closed instantly, healed with no scar.

Warmed in God's hand, the rib changed and grew, swiftly whirling, growing and growing till it was not a bone, but a new creature, breathing with life, standing on small, bare feet in the grass.

The first woman was made.

God could have made her from dust, as He made Adam. He could have made her from nothing. But He wanted Adam to have a companion who was really part of him.

Adam sighed in his sleep, and turned and woke. He saw

the woman God had made for him. And Adam cried out with love and joy.

Together they stood, Adam so tall and strong, she so graceful and soft, needing each other, loving each other in the sight of God, as men and women were always to do. Eve, he would call her, which meant "Life," because she was mother of all living, and with Eve, come what may, he need never again be lonely.

Together they thanked God, and praised Him, and then, together still, they went about in Paradise, perfectly happy. They had everything anyone could want. The animals served them, and played with them. Adam and Eve took care of the Garden and loved each other and their God. And day followed day, each one gleaming with new joy.

"Nothing will ever happen to spoil this garden," said Eve.

"Nothing," agreed Adam. "So long as we love God."

One afternoon Eve sat by herself in the Garden under the trees.

Overhead a branch swayed and dipped. Then with a swift drop a serpent slid to the ground before her, graceful and glittering. Part of him lay coiled in the grass. The rest of him, green with golden rings, rose before her, curving like a stem of some strange flower with his narrow head and long thin tongue as the blossom.

The serpent spoke to Eve, and she did not think it strange, for with the gifts God had given Adam and Eve they could understand all living things. Indeed they did not even need words to speak to each other, this first man and woman, for they knew each other's thoughts.

"Is it true," the serpent asked, "that God does not allow you to eat the fruit of every tree in Paradise?"

"No!" said Eve. "Adam and I may eat of any tree except one."

"Which one?"

"God has commanded us not to eat the fruit of the Tree of Knowledge of Good and Evil," answered Eve.

"But why?" asked the serpent with an impudent grin. "That is the most delicious fruit of all, you know."

"All I know is that we must obey God. Besides He said we should surely die if we ate that fruit."

The serpent threw back his head and laughed, the nastiest, most scornful laughter that ever shook the treetops of Eden. Eve shivered to hear it. Never before had any creature dared laugh at God!

The serpent took a deep breath. "You shall not die if you eat that fruit, Eve."

Closer he came, to whisper in her ear, and his words were a monstrous, cunning lie. "If you ate that fruit you would become as wise as God, knowing all good and evil. That is why God does not want you to taste it. He does not want you and Adam to become as wise as He! Eat it, Eve. Taste it. Why should God forbid you? Why must you obey Him?"

Eve looked at the tree closely. Until now she had hardly thought about it. *Was what the serpent said true?* she wondered.

Closer and closer she moved to the tree, and stopped, five steps away from the shaggy brown trunk. *If I do eat it will I really be as wise as God?* she wondered. What could be so wrong about eating one piece of fruit?

God has forbidden it, and He is the Lord, her conscience said. Eve looked over her shoulder. The serpent stared at her and grinned. Then he slithered away into the forest, leaving her alone to decide.

Eve stepped nearer to the tree, lifted her hand, and let her fingers curl over the fruit. One little tug she gave it, and the twig flew upward, leaving the fruit moist and chill in her hand.

She knew it was wrong, and she did not care. Pride and disobedience made her soft cheeks hard. On that afternoon Eve sinned, the first sin of the world by disobeying God. She loved God, but she loved herself more, so she did what *she* wanted to do.

She opened her mouth and bit into the fruit. It tasted sharp on her tongue, but she would not spit it out. She chewed it, and it was bitter, and she swallowed it.

"Eve!"

From the forest Adam ran toward her, his face white with horror. He looked around fearfully, expecting at any moment to see God storm down upon them. But the Garden was quiet, absolutely still.

Then Eve told him what the serpent had said. The half-eaten fruit was still in her hand. Adam opened his mouth. He wanted to scold her, to scream at her, to tell her how monstrous a thing she had done, to break the law of God, Who loved them. But Adam looked at the fruit and he thought to himself: *Now Eve has dared what I am afraid to do, and perhaps she will be as wise as God.*

Adam wanted that fruit. And he took it from Eve, and ate it.

Darkness came to the Garden. The air grew chill, and they shivered and were cold. And they realized that the world looked different now that they had eaten of the knowledge of good and evil. Before, there had been only good, only happiness. Now worries and problems seemed to crawl through their minds, and fear sprang into being. They looked at each other with uneasy, lonely eyes.

They were glad it was dark, for they were uncomfortable with each other and they wanted to hide. Suddenly, for the first time since God made them, they were embarrassed that they wore no clothes, and without a word they picked some big thick fig leaves and put them together to make themselves aprons.

"Adam!"

The Voice of God called. They were terrified, and they hid in the forest.

"Where are you, Adam?"

From the thickest shadows Adam answered. "I heard Your Voice and I was afraid, because I was naked, and I hid myself."

"Who told you that you were naked? Have you eaten of the Tree that I commanded you not to touch?"

Crouching under the tree, next to Eve, Adam trembled. He was afraid to take the full blame. He was a coward, and he said: "The woman *You* gave to be with me, *she* gave me the fruit. And I did eat."

God said to the woman, "Why have you done this?"

"The serpent deceived me," said Eve.

Then God spoke to the green and gold serpent swaying in the forest. "Because you have done this thing, you are cursed among all beasts of the earth. You shall crawl upon your breast, and your mouth shall be filled with dust. I will make you and the woman enemies, and your children's children and hers. She shall crush your head, and you shall lie in wait for her heel."

And Eve was glad to hear God speak so to the serpent. Then God, Who knew she could not simply blame the tempter, turned to her and said: "I will give you many sorrows. In sorrow shall you bring forth children, and you shall be under your husband's power, and he shall rule over you."

Then to Adam, who could not simply blame Eve, God said: "Because you listened to your wife, and ate of the Tree, which I forbade you, cursed is your work in the earth. With labor and sweat shall you get your bread all the days of your life."

For a moment all was silent. Then God said: "I made you from the earth. To the earth you shall return. Dust you are, and to dust you shall return."

Just so, through sin, death came in the world. In His goodness, God had given Adam and Eve the power to live forever. And they had mocked His goodness, and broken His law, and had not loved Him with a whole heart. So God had taken back His gift. Adam and Eve would not live forever. Someday they must die and be buried in the dust. And so too it would be for all men and women who came after them.

Gone now were all the special powers God had given Adam and Eve, the grace which He had meant all their children to share. They had not loved God enough to obey Him. They had not been worthy of the gifts of His love.

God made clothes of animal skins for Adam and Eve, and sent them out of the Garden of Eden into the strange, unfriendly world.

Before them stretched a road through high new gates, a road leading into darkness, and loneliness, and the terrors of the night. The gates clanged shut behind them, and Adam and Eve were alone.

Through the gates they looked at the paradise they had lost. They could see in the middle of the Garden the gaunt brown arms of the Tree of Knowledge of Good and Evil. Beside the Tree stood an angel on guard with a flaming sword, turning in every direction.

But the Garden was empty of God. No longer would He walk its paths. Adam and Eve walked into the darkness, out on the savage earth.

And no one, man, woman, or child, living in this world would ever find the way into the Garden again, because Adam and Eve had disobeyed the Lord.

The First Rainbow

No one in town could understand what the old man was doing, or why.

They would climb to his farm, to the neat little mud house where he lived with his wife, and his three sons and their wives, and shake their heads. Out in front of the house, where the corn used to grow in neat rows, the old man was building a thing larger than all the houses in town put together.

There was not even a stream nearby, not a brook or a lake or a pond. The only water anyone could see was in the well. And yet obviously this thing he was building was some kind of boat.

"The old man is crazy!" they whispered. "He has lost his mind!"

Then they looked behind the house, where once the six sheep and nine cows had grazed, and where the old man's wife had dried the figs and dates to be stored. But now, as far as the eye could see, and the nose could smell, the fields were filled with animals and birds.

In cages, and in houses, in barns and behind fences, animals were braying and bleating and snorting and growling, roaring and cooing and twittering and snuffling. And scurrying among them with their arms full of food were the old man's wife and her three daughters-in-law, back and forth, back and forth, feeding and watering each one all day.

"Oh, those poor women!" said the people from town.

"Where in the world did all the animals come from?"

"And why?"

The bravest of them, swaggering a little, went together to ask the old man himself. They found him under a fig tree, eating his noonday bread and cheese.

"Noah," they said, "what nonsense is this, building a boat on dry land, and collecting the beasts of the wild?"

Noah looked at them gravely over his cloud-white beard.

"I shall tell you," he said in his gentle voice. "You will not believe me, but I shall tell you."

They sat on the grass to listen.

"I was here, under this same tree, alone. And suddenly a Voice spoke to me, a Voice that seemed to come from the clouds and from the earth. And it was the Voice of God," said Noah.

The men looked at each other. The Voice of God, indeed! And they winked and smirked at each other, for these men did not think much about God at all.

"God spoke to me," said Noah very quietly. "He said that the world was full of the evil and wickedness of man. And He said that He would destroy man, because He was sorry He had ever made man. And He would destroy all the living things on the earth, and save only a few, and with those few He would start again."

The men on the grass snorted with nasty cackles of laughter.

"Destroy us? Because we are evil? And how will God do this, Noah? Tell us!"

"He will bring a flood, and cover the whole earth. That is why He told me to build this boat, which He called an ark. He told me exactly how to build it. And in it I am to put two of each wild animal, and seven of each of those animals which men use, and keep them safe while all other things are destroyed."

One man giggled. "Noah, you *are* crazy. All your life you've been peculiar. You're always talking about some God no one has ever seen. You're always working, as if work were important. And you don't have any fun. Always worrying about being good, and just, and pure, whatever that means. No wonder you're losing your mind."

"God said——" began Noah.

"God said!" The men scrambled to their feet. Their faces in the noonday sun were cruel and sickly pale, twisted with the wickedness of their hearts. "Who cares about your God?"

And the truth was that in their souls there was no room for God, for they were filled with sin and hatred, and the creeping sickness of evil. They turned and walked away from Noah, and took their wives and children with them, and spat on the ark.

Under the fig tree Noah wept.

"I will destroy man from the face of the earth, and the evil he has made," God had said.

Noah understood why.

Months passed into years, and still Noah and his family worked, collecting the animals, caring for them, and building the ark. Time did not mean much to Noah. He had already had more than five hundred birthdays, and he could expect to live many more years. His grandfather, after all, was

Methuselah, the oldest man in the world, who had lived to see nine hundred and sixty-nine!

Even for a skilled carpenter like Noah building the ark was no easy task. According to God's directions, it was to be 450 feet long, and 75 feet wide and 45 feet high, with three stories, or decks, in it, and many little rooms. That would make the ark about half as big as the liner *Queen Mary* today, and there were only Noah and his three sons to build it, in the time they could spare from their ordinary daily chores.

And the zoo! cows, lambs, chickens, these anyone could handle. But Noah's wife and his three daughters-in-law must also nurse elephants, lions, scorpions, spiders, caterpillars, mice, cats, even snakes, and all the other kinds of animals of the world.

And in all these hard, lonely, tiring years they heard no more the Voice of God. More than once the little family was tempted to forget the whole idea of the ark, turn loose the squalling, restless, smelly animals, and live again in peace like ordinary folk. But each morning and each night they prayed to the silent God. And each day they worked again until at last the ark was finished, and Noah was six hundred years old.

Twilight purpled the hills as Noah walked through the rows of wooden cages watering the beasts for the night. The cackling and the bleating, the snuffling and the humming and the twittering stopped, and night brought silence.

Then, from the moon-washed wind came the Voice of God:

"Noah! Go into the ark, you and your family, for I have seen that of all men living you are the only ones who are good, and true to your God. Take the animals with you. And after seven days I will rain upon the earth for forty days and forty nights, and I will destroy everything else I have made from the face of the earth."

The next morning Noah led them into the ark, the parade of animals and birds and creeping things first, and then his family, with their pots and pitchers, and loom and spindle, their clothes and their tools, and his wife's sacks of flower and vegetable seeds.

The sun shone brilliantly. Not a cloud could be seen. And the men and women of the town stood around the ark pointing their fingers and howling with laughter.

"Where is your flood, Noah?"

"Tell me, old man, are you seasick here on dry land?"

"Noah, where is this God Who is going to destroy us all?"

"Give Noah a jug of well water to float his ship!"

Noah tried to tell them, tried to make them understand. He begged them to turn from evil, and not to offend God any longer with their lies and their filth and their stealing, and the blasphemy of their tongues.

But the sun shone day after day for the whole week. And the men who hated God sniggered and spat, and made fun of Noah. They did not listen, and they did not believe.

On the seventh day the sky clouded.

By midday thunder rolled. Noah closed the windows and

the door of the ark. Still the men and women laughed out-side.

"We've seen thunder and rain before!" they cried. "This doesn't prove a thing."

The rain came gently, then harder, a silver-gray rain of death, a drizzle becoming a downpour and then a torrent, steady, purposeful, relentless as the hand of God.

Rain—then suddenly, unseen in the blinding fall of the floodgates of heaven, the waters of the seas broke forth, coiling up from the land, loosing the fountains of the deep. The earth was covered, lost in the cleansing fury of the waters.

Forty days and forty nights the rain fell, water from above

and water rising from below, washing over even the highest mountains of earth. The black, wet sky met the wild blackness of the waves and there was nothing but darkness and death on earth.

But inside the ark there was warmth, and life, and the light of pottery lamps with flaxen wicks burning in oil. And in the ark was the warmth and light of God, in the hearts of the chosen ones, of Noah and his family.

Noah's wife sat in the ark, her hands busy with the threads of a cloak she was weaving for Noah—but when would he wear it, and where?

"Outside of us no one lives in the whole world," she said sadly. "It's a lonesome thought, and a fearsome one."

"God chose us to build a new world," said Noah's son Shem, his dark eyes solemn under his thick brows. "And you, Father, you'll be the father of the whole human race."

"A new Adam you'll be," said his curly-bearded brother Japheth.

"I pray God helps us to stay close to Him, and make a good world," said Noah quietly.

And during those forty days and forty nights their thoughts went back hundreds of years to the first man and woman, to Adam and Eve, who had sinned against God in the Garden of Eden.

Then on the forty-first day, the rain no longer beat on the roof of the ark. Noah opened the window. Under the sullen, swollen sky stretched an ocean without a shore, endless and gray.

Day after day the ark drifted with its animals and its eight living souls, without land or star to steer by, and nowhere to go. One hundred and fifty days, five months, the ark drifted.

Then a wind rose and blew its drying breath upon the waters, and slowly they grew less. Inside the ark the birds fluttered and beat their wings against their cages. The elephants trumpeted and the lions paced restlessly, while the spiders spun their webs, and the frogs hopped back and forth. The piles of hay and grain and raw meat for the animals grew lower day by day.

Noah's records showed that it was early autumn, and nine months had passed, when as he peered through the window the cry burst from his lips:

"Land! See—a mountaintop. There above the waves!"

But only the barest tips of rock showed over the waters. Again the little family must wait, and calm the panting animals, and stretch the little supply of food.

Forty more days they waited. Then Noah said: "Perhaps somewhere, farther than we can see, the land is dry." From the room of birds Noah chose a raven, with strong black wings, and, opening the window, set him free to scout for dry land.

The raven never came back.

One week later Noah chose a gentle white dove, and sent her out over the waters.

"Surely now there is land for us," said Noah.

But at evening the dove returned, for she had not found one place to rest on the whole watery earth.

Seven more days he waited before he sent the dove out again. Off she flew into the sky, far, far out of sight, then suddenly, wondrously she was back, and in her beak she carried a joyous sign—an olive branch, living, and in leaf.

"God be praised!" cried Noah.

And soon a grating rumble shook the ark, and the flat bottom came to rest on the earth, and the waters dried up. The flood was over.

Noah peered out the window. The ark had come to rest

on a high peak, the top of Mount Ararat, which is in the land we today call Turkey.

"Noah! Go out of the ark, and go upon the earth, and people it." The Voice of God came clear in the morning wind.

Two by two the family stepped down onto solid ground, for the first time in more than a year.

The earth was new, fresh and clean after the baptism of the flood. Brave new grass grew on the hillsides, and the buds of a new spring covered the trees. The air was sweet, clean as dawn.

Noah opened the rooms of the ark. In a flurry and a flutter and a whirring of wings the birds burst loose, nightingales and eagles, sparrows and larks, singing a welcome to the blue sky. Hurrying, stampeding, frisking and bounding, the animals tumbled out, eager to adventure into the new world. Down the mountainsides they went.

"Hurry!" called Noah to his sons. "Hurry! Before anything else, we must build an altar to God!"

And when the altar was built, Noah remembered how so long ago Abel's sacrifice had pleased God. So Noah took two fine cows and two fat chickens and burned them on the altar, as a sacrifice to God.

And God blessed Noah and his sons, and spoke to them.

"Never again will I curse the earth because man is evil. The days of the earth, seedtime and harvest, cold and heat, summer and winter, night and day, shall not cease.

"Behold I will make a covenant with you, a promise to you and to all men who shall live after you. Never again will a flood lay waste the earth."

God's Voice grew gentler, closer to the green-cloaked earth, and the eight men and women who were to people it.

"And this is the sign of the covenant, the sign of My promise," said the Lord, "which I give to you and to all living souls forever. I will set My rainbow in the clouds, and it shall be the sign. And when I shall cover the sky with clouds, My bow shall appear in the clouds, and I shall remember, and there shall no more be waters of a flood to destroy all flesh."

And suddenly God flung His rainbow across the sky, arched high from heaven to earth, sparkling in wondrous color, the promise of God's love for man. Noah looked up to see the bridge of light, and tears of joy filled his eyes.

"A promise forever," he whispered as his long white beard flew in the bright new breeze.

Thousands of years have passed since that day. Noah and his sons and his sons' sons traveled across the face of the earth and peopled it, with God's blessing.

And still, to this day, God's rainbow shines in the skies, the silent, glowing promise, the bridge of glory between heaven and earth.

"Abraham!"

"Nothing," said Sarai, "ever happens to us."

And, like the good housewife she was, Sarai began carefully to sweep the crumbs after the evening meal.

Abram, her husband, smiled. "Nothing, Sarai. Ours is a quiet life. We do not travel. We are not rich. We will never be famous. God has not even given us a child! I suppose nothing exciting will ever happen to us."

But Abram was wrong. He did not know it, but God had chosen him for a tremendous adventure, which would begin that night.

Abram was the great-great-great-great-great-great-great grandson of Noah. Nine generations stood between him and the ark builder, and in those years most of the family, indeed a great deal of the world, had turned away from the Lord. Some people had invented their own fairy-tale gods, and built hideous idols with twisted faces and the bodies of beasts, and prayed to them. But Abram worshiped only the one true God, the God Who created the world, and made men, and made you and me. And God had watched Abram closely, and had seen that he was good.

Abram stood a while after dinner this night in the courtyard of his house, counting the stars. Suddenly, over the clatter of the pots and the hum of voices in the street, came one Voice, clear, deep, and beautiful. And without being told, Abram knew it was the Voice of God. He fell to his knees.

"Abram!" said the Lord. "Leave this country behind you, and come away into a land I will show you. I will make you the father of a great nation. I will bless you, and make your name famous. And your name shall be a blessing for the world."

But how, Lord? Shall we really have a child, which we want so much? And where will we go? And why choose me?

These questions bubbled in Abram's mind, but the Voice was gone, the Lord had withdrawn, and Abram was alone, with work to do. He must obey, even without knowing why or how.

Into the house to tell Sarai he must go, to pack and make his plans. Many, many are the people who must go with them. Their nephew. Abram's brother's son, whose name was Lot, and Lot's wife, and all Abram's servants and friends and helpers must travel with them. And they must have many donkeys and camels to carry all their possessions, their clothes, and furniture, and tools, and the kitchen things and food.

"*Where* are we going, Uncle Abram?" Lot demanded. "You cannot simply go, without knowing where!"

"God will show us," said Abram.

In the chill of dawn they left. Abram, wrapped in his red woolen cloak, led the way as he thought God meant them to go, into the blue-skied spaces of the south. Month after weary month they traveled, through mountains and deserts, through lush green valleys and along the sea, year after year, all the way to Egypt, and back north again. Each morning and each night they prayed. And finally, when no one but Abram could have faced one more day of travel, God told Abram that the place had been found. He was to make his home here, in the land of Canaan, in the place called Bethel.

As long as they had traveled, Abram and Lot had no trouble. But now that the long struggle of the journey was over, Lot was dissatisfied and he began to grumble and quarrel.

"There is not room here for your sheep and mine too, Abram," growled Lot. "And your men get in the way of my men."

Abram smiled kindly. "Let us not quarrel, Lot. See, here is the whole land before you. Choose whichever part you want, and we will separate, you one way and I the other."

Lot looked carefully around. One part, the great hollow of Jordan, seemed to him the greenest, the richest, and the finest. He grinned greedily. "I choose that land!"

Abram let him have it, with a smile and a blessing. And Lot and his wife went off with their sheep and their cows, their herdsmen and their servants, sure that they had made the best of that bargain.

When Lot had gone, the Lord said to Abram:

"Look about you. Turn your eyes to north and south, to east and west. All the land that you see I give to you, and to your children and your children's children forever. Journey through the land at ease. To you I will give it."

So Abram moved his tent, and went to live in the valley of Hebron. And there he built an altar to the Lord.

Now, he thought, he would have no more worries. The people of this land were kind and friendly, and he and Sarai and their household could live in peace.

Watching the moonrise on starry nights, Abram would sometimes wonder how Lot was making out. Lot and his wife had moved, so Abram had heard, to a city named Sodom, and were running their farms from a distance. And how could they enjoy Sodom? Abram had heard ugly tales of that place. Evil grew in Sodom like a scarlet weed, strangling the air itself with poison. *Surely trouble would fall on a good man in Sodom,* thought Abram, and he shivered in the night air.

Then one day came disastrous news.

A messenger, in bloody and battle-torn clothes, rode out of the east. "Four kings have come and conquered our land. They have sacked our cities, and stolen all our wealth. And your nephew Lot is a prisoner."

Abram loved peace. He had no use for war. But his duty was clear. He must rescue Lot. Abram gathered together the men of his country, three hundred and eighteen untrained men who never had been soldiers. He sharpened swords and spears, and led his little army into battle. And, being a clever man, he fell on the enemy at night, creeping on them in surprise. And Abram defeated the four kings, turning himself into something he never expected to be, a conqueror of cities.

A strange conqueror he was, by soldiers' standards. He broke the bolts on the cells where Lot was caged. He gave back to Lot his wealth, which the kings had stolen. And then Abram simply went home. He did not loot the lands he had conquered. He did not take one souvenir of his victory. He did not want revenge or gold. He wanted only peace.

"Silly old man!" the soldiers called him. "What kind of conqueror is he to give up the spoils of winning? He could have been rich!"

But once again God came to Abram saying: "Fear not, Abram, I am your shield and will protect you. Your reward will be great indeed."

As Abram hurried homeward, he passed a city built on a hill of enormous black boulders. In those days it was called

Salem, but we call the same place Jerusalem. The king of Salem was a holy gray-haired man named Melchisedech, who was also a priest of the most high God. And, seeing Abram, Melchisedech suddenly came out to meet him, bringing bread and wine, from which he made a sacrifice to God, and gave Abram blessing. For Melchisedech knew that God had secret plans for Abram.

Later, when Abram was home again with Sarai, God came to him in a vision, and, taking Abram out of doors, He said: "Look up at the sky, and count, if you can, the stars in it. Your children, and the nation springing from you shall be numberless as those stars."

Abram believed God, and trusted Him. And that was very difficult to do. After all, Abram was eighty-six years old, and Sarai too was old, and people of their age do not usually have babies. How could it be, then, that they should have a family that would become as numberless as the stars or the grains of dust on the ground?

Sarai sat with Abram at the door of the tent, and tears ran down her wrinkled face, for she longed to have a child.

Soon, very soon, a baby was born in Abram's tent, but it was not Sarai's child. Hagar, Sarai's young and beautiful handmaid, had a baby boy, and he was called Ismael.

"Perhaps Ismael is the child the Lord meant," said Sarai sadly.

"Perhaps," said Abram.

Ismael grew to be a wild lad, strong and fierce. No one could tame him or make him obey. And for thirteen years Abram wondered if this was what God had intended, and God was silent. As always, the Lord expected those who loved Him to be patient. Abram was certainly learning patience.

He was ninety-nine years old before God spoke again, and

what a strange message was that! "Listen, Abram, for your name is to be changed!

"You are to be the father of a multitude of nations. No longer shall your name be Abram. You shall be called Abraham, which means 'the father of a throng.'

"And you shall call your wife not Sarai, but Sara, which means 'the princess.'"

At noon the next day Abraham, who used to be Abram, sat by his tent door wondering about his new name. He looked up and saw what seemed to be three men standing near him. But they were not men. Two were angels, and the third was the Lord God Himself!

Abraham ran to meet them, bowing down to the earth, and inviting them to come in and rest, and eat and drink. And they agreed.

Abraham was trembling with excitement and wonder and fear. The Lord God Himself was his guest!

Quickly he ran to find Sara, to ask her to cook some cakes. And he ran to the barn to fetch a calf, tender and well fed, and gave it to a servant.

"Roast this on the spit, quickly—but do not burn it, and do not undercook it!"

Abraham's face was red with hurrying. And Sara was so nervous she couldn't even come out of the tent. Such a hurrying and flurrying and scurrying there was inside the main tent and the cooking tents and in the fields, till finally the meal was ready. Abraham himself served it, and stood beside his guests as they ate in the shade of the trees.

When they had finished, the Lord asked:

"Where is your wife, Sara?"

"She is here, in the tent," Abraham answered.

"I will come back," said He Who was speaking to him, "next

year without fail. And this time next year, your wife Sara shall have a son."

Now Sara was eavesdropping behind the tent door, still too shy to come out, and too curious to go away. And Sara, although she was really a good woman, had, after all, been hearing promises for years that she would have a child, and nothing had ever come of all the promises. Already she was ninety years old, and never had she even heard of a woman having a baby when she was that old!

So—sad to say—Sara heard what the Lord said, and Sara giggled. She giggled, and then she laughed out loud, and even though she clapped her hands over her mouth, the sputtering of her laugh could be heard very clearly.

The Lord turned to Abraham. "Why does Sara laugh? And why does she ask whether she is indeed to become a mother in her old age? Can anything be too difficult for the Lord? At this time next year I will come back, and Sara shall have a son."

Sara turned pale with terror, and burst from the tent. "Indeed, Lord. I did not laugh!" she lied. "Nothing is impossible for You."

"Ah," said the Lord, "but you did laugh." Yet He was not angry, for He knew the goodness of Sara, and He forgave her.

And one year later, at the very time God had foretold, Sara had a child. The Lord returned to their tent, and a baby boy was born when Abraham was one hundred years old.

Sara took the baby in her arms, and she cried out, "God has made me laugh with joy. And so I shall call him Isaac, which means 'laughter.' For all who hear of this will laugh for joy with me."

Many years God had tested Abraham, mysterious years of wandering and of waiting, of promises that seemed never to be answered. Abraham had remained steadfast and true. And for everyone who trusts God, and is patient, the reward is very great.

Now Abraham had his reward. He and Sara had a son. And Isaac and his sons, and his sons' sons would become, as God said, numberless as the stars.

The secret was in the waiting, and the trusting, and in the loving of God.

The Strange Test

Abraham the wise, Abraham the ancient, Abraham the specially chosen friend of God, had a son. Never did any father love his child more than Abraham loved little laughing Isaac.

He would look at the boy and remember all the lonely years when he and his wife Sara had longed for a child. He would remember the day the Lord and His angels had come to his tent, and eaten under his shade trees, and promised that he and Sara would have a son, a baby in their old age. Isaac—the son God had promised!

Abraham had counted a hundred birthdays before Isaac was born. His beard was white as sea foam and his face cracked with wrinkles like sun-baked clay. But he was still strong and hale as a young man.

As Isaac grew, he was constantly at his father's side, learning the ways of men and of God. Abraham taught Isaac how to care for sheep, to shear them, how to make tents and water bags from their skins, taught him how to ride, and to build, and to watch the skies for coming weather.

And he taught his son how to love God. He would tell Isaac the great true stories of the past, of Adam and Eve, who betrayed God's goodness to them, of their sons, Cain and Abel, of Noah, and the rest. So well did Isaac know these that he could have drawn a map of the Garden of Eden.

"What is the most important thing in the world, Isaac?" Abraham would ask.

"To love God," Isaac would answer. "To love Him so completely that you would obey Him without question, no matter what He asked."

Neither Abraham nor little Isaac knew how fiercely God would test their love.

Isaac took pride in helping his father with the sacrifices the family made to honor the Lord.

As was the custom, approved by God, they would sacrifice yearling lambs. They would kill the lambs on altars built of field stone, and burn them over hot faggot fires. They made a holocaust of the lambs, which means that they burned them till they were completely consumed, and nothing was left. Always they picked the best and most valuable lambs to offer God, for a sacrifice meant giving up something truly precious.

The years went by, golden and peaceful. Isaac grew to be a fine young lad with curly dark hair and long, strong legs. And Abraham thanked God each day for His goodness and His blessings.

Then, one windy afternoon as Abraham trudged alone across a brown and fallow field, he suddenly heard the Voice of God speaking for the first time since Isaac was born:

"Abraham!"

The old man halted in the wind-swept field, his eyes eager with happiness. "I am here, Lord."

"Abraham! Take Isaac, your beloved son, to a mountain

which I shall show you in the land of Moriah. And there—
offer him for a sacrifice, a burnt offering on the altar."

The old man's heart almost stopped beating.

*Oh, Voice of Almighty God—You cannot mean what I have
heard? My son? My Isaac? My dearly beloved? Isaac to be
burned like a beast on the altar? I am having a nightmare.*

It was no dream. The Lord, the one God, the true God, the
only God, had spoken to His servant Abraham. Now Abraham
must ask himself the most difficult question of all:

Do I love God more than anyone or anything else in the
world? Or do I love Isaac more than God?

Never had God given anyone a harder test. Abraham, who
loved Isaac so dearly, and God so deeply, must choose. God
had asked him to sacrifice his son, for Him.

Now, would he obey?

For the rest of that day and night, Abraham walked alone.
At dusk he waved away his bowl of milk and wheaten loaves.
He could not eat. His eyes were round with sadness. His
cheeks twitched nervously. He paced in the darkness outside
his tent. And when Isaac came to kiss him good night Abraham shuddered, and turned his back, and waved at the lad
to go away.

Then, when the night was blackest, and all were asleep,
Abraham made his decision. Into the darkness he shouted his
orders:

"Up! Isaac and two menservants—up! By dawn we leave
for a distant place."

And Abraham said not a word about where or why they
were going.

At his orders they loaded a pile of wood faggots on the back
of a young gray ass and set out. Three days they traveled
across the shining plain of Mamre, and up into the thickly
wooded hills.

And not once did Abraham speak to his son. The old man's browned face was like a mask of stone. The deep gleam in his eyes was like a fire in the depth of a cave.

At a clearing near the mountaintop Abraham ordered his two servants to remain with the gray ass, while he and Isaac went alone to offer worship and sacrifice to God. Then Isaac took the firewood on his own back, and trudged after his father still higher toward the bald, deserted peak of Mount Moriah. Still they had not spoken.

At last the boy Isaac dared break the silence.

"Father?"

"What is it, my son?"

"We have the wood to burn the sacrifice. But where is the lamb?"

Abraham closed his eyes and groaned as he answered: "My son, God will see to it that He has an offering for the sacrifice."

The boy said nothing else. He could not see where anyone would find a lamb here on a deserted mountain peak. He could not understand why they had come so far and so suddenly to a place where no altar had been built.

Nor could it have entered his head that these faggots he carried were to burn under his own body, or that his father carried in his sleeve a knife with which to cut his throat—at God's command.

At last they reached the peak. Both were panting, out of breath. But Abraham did not dare to rest. He was afraid even to stop a moment, lest he break down and disobey God. Even now he wanted to scream, to cry out to the heavens against this fiery and bloody sacrifice. *My God, my God, how can You ask me to do this?*

His hands shook so that he could hardly lift the stones to make the altar, but Isaac helped him.

The boy saw how his father was quaking. Something was wrong. His question flew back again: *Where was the lamb to be sacrificed?* One look at Abraham, and without being told Isaac knew the answer. His father's broken heart shone through the tears in his eyes.

Isaac's cheeks turned white. His eyes rolled back. And he cried, he screamed. But he was the obedient son of an obedient father. He held out his hands. He could not understand why God should order such a thing, but he loved Him enough to obey without understanding.

Abraham tied Isaac's wrists and then his ankles with leather thongs, and still not a word between them.

Weeping, Abraham lifted his son, so warm, so yielding, and laid him upon the mound of faggots on the altar. A jerk of the arm, a clutch of fingers around a flashing blade, and there it is, quivering high in the air, the knife in Abraham's hand.

And then, in that tremulous moment, the Voice:

"Abraham! Abraham!"

"Lord, I am here," faltered the old man.

"Do not hurt the lad! Let him alone! I know now that you fear God. You would indeed have killed your only son for My sake. Now set him free. I will not ask it of you!"

The knife fell harmlessly from Abraham's hand.

Eyes streaming with tears, Abraham fell on his son and kissed him, and untied him and lifted him down. Together they stood, in one long embrace.

"My God! My son!" whispered Abraham, over and over, as he stroked the dark curls.

Suddenly, incongruously, another sound troubled the mountaintop—the unmistakable call of an angry ram.

Abraham and Isaac turned and looked. There in a thicket beyond the piled stone altar was a white ram caught by the

horns in the branches. Where no sheep ever ventured stood one ready for sacrifice, led there by God's own design.

Abraham and Isaac came down the mountain together, hand in hand. Smoke still rose from the altar behind them, where they had sacrificed the ram. The gray curls of it rose heavenward, silently speaking of love and honor and thanksgiving to the Lord.

The day would come when a Father would sacrifice His only begotten Son, a Son born into the long line of descendants from Abraham and Isaac. But men had much to learn before they could understand the tremendous meaning of that sacrifice.

Abraham and Isaac had learned part of the truth that day on the mountain. They knew then as never before that, if a man gives all to God, he receives God in return, and God's love, which passes understanding.

The Blessing
in
Disguise

Abraham was dead. And his son Isaac was left with a mystery.

Abraham had lived one hundred and seventy-five years, faithfully serving God. Each command of the Lord he had followed from the day he and his wife Sara had left their home to the fateful moment on the mountain when he had even been ready to sacrifice his beloved Isaac if God willed it.

And God had rewarded His servant Abraham. He had made Abraham the founder of a specially chosen people. From Abraham's family would come the people chosen by God to learn His ways, and prepare the children of earth to become the children of heaven.

Isaac buried Abraham, and wept for him, but one question plagued his mind.

"God told my father that his children's children would be as numberless as the stars of heaven. But I am his son—and I have no children at all!"

And Isaac would sit with his beauteous wife Rebecca, and wonder in the twilight. Theirs was a happy marriage. They loved each other deeply, but year after year was passing, and God had not yet given them a child.

Could He have forgotten His word? There was a mystery indeed.

The answer came, as always, in God's good time. Isaac and Rebecca became the parents, not of one son, but two. Twins were born when all hope seemed gone.

Rebecca held the two boy babies close to her heart. She kissed their ears and their toes, and crooned to them.

"This one, the first of the two, shall be called Esau," said Isaac. "See, his skin is covered with hair, and Esau means 'hairy,' as you know." The father laughed as he studied the infant. "How red he is, Rebecca."

"And this one? What shall we call him?"

"His name shall be Jacob, because he is a 'wrestler'—and see, already he seems to be struggling with his brother. Look, how he holds Esau's heel!"

Rebecca hugged Jacob closer to her. So pink he was, and smooth-skinned, so different from Esau.

"Abraham would have been proud to see these grandchildren," mused Isaac. "May they be as pleasing to God as he was!"

Rebecca was silent a long moment. Then slowly she said: "Isaac, my dear one, there is a great secret I must tell you. Before they were born, these little twins, I heard the Voice of God speaking in my heart."

"What did the Lord say to you?"

"He said: 'These children are to be two different nations. And one shall be stronger than the other. And the elder shall serve the younger.'"

But as the boys grew, it was hard to believe such a prophecy.

Surely one was stronger than the other.

Esau, the elder twin, was rugged and fierce, a tree climber, a camel-back rider, a hunter. Jacob, the younger, was slim and gentle, not a weakling, but a dreamer, kindly and quiet.

They were rivals from the beginning. Esau, with his bluff red face and his thick hair, was his father's favorite. After a day of hunting he would come back to tell old Isaac tales of his adventures and his bold exploits. And Isaac, who was a quiet man, was proud of Esau's vigor and his careless, jolly ways, and loved him.

Jacob was his mother's favorite. She watched him as he grew in wisdom. She saw that Jacob had a strength of mind and soul that noisy Esau did not have.

One day she spoke of this to Isaac. "Esau is our elder son—by three minutes," she said. "But he is not fit to be the elder son. By our law the first-born has the birthright—the most important dignity a man can have. When you are dead he will be the head of the family, owner of all you possess."

"That is so. It has always been so," said Isaac, fingering his stone-gray beard.

"But because of the birthright the elder son must be the wise one. He must decide all the arguments in the family. He must be priestly, for he must lead the household in serving God. And Isaac—our Esau is not a priestly man!"

Isaac growled in his beard. "Esau is a good son. A little wild, but good. And he is the first-born."

"He's a fine man, but he is more interested in playing than in serving God!" said Rebecca. "Isaac, could you not change things? Give the birthright to Jacob?"

"I could. But I will not. Jacob's a splendid lad, but he's too thoughtful. He's no leader. And Esau—Esau is a man among men."

Isaac, bent with age, his eyes dim, hobbled to the fire. "Esau is the elder. His is the birthright. And that is the end of that!"

Meanwhile, at that same instant out in the far fields, the brothers met after their day's work.

Jacob, who was the family shepherd and farmer, bent over a fire of twigs in the open. On the hill nearby sheep grazed. The hand plow stood at the end of eighty straight rows of newly planted wheat. Jacob had worked since sunup. Now in a pot over the fire a lentil stew simmered gently as Jacob stirred.

Suddenly a shadow fell across his hands. Brother Esau loomed before him, then threw his enormous body down on the ground, exhausted after a long, unlucky hunt. His good-natured green eyes looked hungrily at the red beans in the bubbling water.

"I'm famished," he groaned in joking despair. "May I have some of the stew?"

Jacob shook his head. "There's just enough for one. You're on your way home and you can eat there. But I must stay with the sheep a good while longer."

"But I'm hungry now. I'd give all I own in the world for a dish of that pottage."

Jacob looked up, startled. "All you own in the world? You should not joke about anything that serious."

"Brother, I mean it. I am starved!"

Jacob's fingers twined nervously. "You wouldn't sell your birthright for a dish of food, Esau. It must mean more to you than that."

"Jacob, my dear brother, you take things too seriously. Name your price, but feed me. If I die of hunger, what good will the birthright do me?"

"The birthright shall be mine?"

"Yours!" said Esau.

"Swear it!" said Jacob solemnly.

Esau swore to it.

He sold his right to the spiritual and physical wealth of his father for a mess of pottage. He traded his blessings for a trifle he craved at the moment.

Jacob told his mother what had happened.

"Is it fair for me to take it, Mother? Esau was foolish. He did not think——"

"If he could sell his birthright so lightly, could he ever take it seriously?" asked his mother. "He would disgrace his father and his God. Of course it is right for it to be yours."

Rebecca, good woman that she was, was not the wisest person in judging right and wrong.

No one told gray-bearded Isaac about the sale of the birthright. Jacob and Rebecca were afraid of his anger. And Esau never thought to mention it at all.

A few weeks later Isaac took to his bed, with the miseries of old age. His sight had grown hazy. His sparkling black eyes were dimmed. His cheeks were thin and drawn.

"Esau!"

"I am here, Father."

"Take your quiver and bow. Go out and hunt for me. Bring me a deer, and let me feast on venison stew. The meat may give me strength. And then you must tell me about the chase. And though I cannot run or walk, though I cannot even see, I shall feel young again listening to you. Then, Esau, I shall give you my blessing before I die, the blessing that is your birthright."

Rebecca heard those words. As Esau hurried away, she called Jacob to her.

"That blessing shall be yours," she whispered. "Listen . . ."

Together they hurried to carry out one of the strangest deceptions of all time.

They killed a kid, a dark-haired baby goat, and Jacob skinned it. Rebecca herself cooked the goat meat, stewing it with herbs over the deep fire pit. And when it was done it did taste a little like venison. A sick man, a nearly toothless old man might never know the difference between goat and deer meat.

Silently Rebecca showed Jacob how to cut the goatskin into strips. Then she fastened two long strips to Jacob's tunic at the shoulder line, wrapping them around the arms till they fitted like sleeves, covering the hands down to the knuckles. One more furry strip she wound around his neck.

"Now," said Rebecca. "Carry this in to your father. And remember all that I told you."

"He may curse me instead of bless me," said Jacob.

"If so, let the curse be on me," said his mother fiercely. "You listen to me, and obey!"

Pale but determined, Jacob obeyed.

"I am here, Father," he said, trying to speak as Esau did. He placed the stew close to the bed. "And here is the venison stew."

"Esau?" whispered Isaac. "How could it be you? How could you have caught a deer so soon, and cooked it?"

"God was with me. I found one not half a mile from home and felled it at once."

"Come to me," ordered Isaac in a firmer tone.

Slowly he ran his hands over his son's arms. "Your voice is the voice of Jacob, but Jacob never was so hairy. These feel like Esau's arms and hands. . . ." His voice faded away into his beard.

"Father?" said Jacob.

"Who are you, my son?"

"I am Esau, your first-born, and I have done as you commanded," lied Jacob. "Give me your blessing, Father."

The old man stared but could not see. Questions passed silently over his face. He sighed.

Then slowly, solemnly, he gave the father's blessing.

"God give you the dew of heaven, and of the fatness of the earth, abundance of corn and wine. And let peoples serve you, and tribes honor you. And let your mother's children bow down before you. Cursed be he that curses you, and let him that blesses you be filled with blessings."

So Jacob received the birthright.

At nightfall Esau returned. A staunch brown deer lay across his shoulders.

"Father," said Esau, "I have come."

The breath of outdoors was about him, the smell of the woods and of trampled ferns, and leather, and the wild smells of hunting. And the voice was Esau's, deep, and hearty as an October wind.

"Esau?"

Weak as he was, Isaac pushed himself up on his elbows. "It is you. And the other was Jacob. Esau, my son, I have given your blessing to Jacob! He deceived me!"

He fell back on a pillow. Anger stirred in him, lashed its tail, and slept again.

Isaac was too old, too wise for anger. He, who had been so close to God all his days, trusted in Him completely. Had he not as a child lain on the altar, ready to die at his own father's hands for God's command? Never since had Isaac mistrusted the things which the Lord allowed to happen, even when he could not understand them.

"In God's wisdom," said Isaac, "good will come of this, even from the lies and the deceit of those so near to me. He will punish them. I need not. And He can bring good even out of evil. Even in doing wrong they must serve Him. That is His wonderful secret. All things serve Him."

Esau snorted. Such talk meant little to him. He flung himself down by the bed, and roared out:

"Bless me also, my father!"

But Isaac was still deep in thought. "I remember now what the Voice said to Rebecca when you two were born. God said then that the younger should rule. How strange are His ways."

"Have you no blessing for me?" cried Esau, clutching his father's arm.

"I blessed your brother. I have made him lord over you. And what shall I do for you, my son?"

"Have you only one blessing, Father? I beseech you, bless me also!" And Esau wept loud bitter tears for the birthright he had sold.

And Isaac blessed Esau. Not with the same blessing he gave to Jacob, for that could be given only once. But with a father's love he gave Esau what he could, which was, of course, what God intended.

It was not what Esau intended. Esau was furious. He swore to kill Jacob.

And when Rebecca heard that, she warned Jacob to leave at once.

"Go to my brother Laban, in the land of Syria, and stay there till Esau's anger passes. And I shall tell your father that you go to seek a good wife who believes in God, and not one of the evil-faced heathen women that Esau would have for a wife."

Isaac, thin and wasted in his bed, called Jacob to him. Jacob was afraid, but Isaac forgave him, as fathers always will. And Isaac blessed him again, and prayed for him, and sent him on his way.

Jacob took a donkey to carry his bags of food and of clothes, of money and of water.

But Jacob himself carried a heavier load than his donkey, the weight of guilt. His father's forgiveness was not enough. Riding onward, eyes on the horizon, he wondered:

"I have done wrong. I have lied. I have cheated. I have stolen, for the blessing did not belong to me. How can God forgive me?"

And as he rode through the bleak hills he prayed, "The God of Isaac my father, the God of Abraham my grandfather— forgive me!"

Lonely and forlorn, Jacob rode, carrying the heavy knowledge of his sin. He would be willing to suffer any punishment if only he knew that the God he loved would forgive him.

He made his camp under the stars that night. He ate the thick brown crusty bread Rebecca had baked, and the cheese that came from the black goats of his father's fields.

Finally, choosing a large smooth stone on which to rest his head, Jacob slept.

And as he slept, God sent him a dream.

The purple-black midnight sky burst open.

A ladder of golden light stretched from heaven to earth, to Jacob's feet. Angels clustered everywhere, dazzling in their whiteness, moving up and down the ladder, restlessly going from heaven to earth and home again.

And the Lord, leaning upon the ladder, spoke to Jacob:

"I am the Lord God of Abraham and the God of Isaac. This land I will give to you and to your children. And your children's children shall be a great nation, and in you all the tribes of earth shall be blessed.

"And I will be your keeper wherever you go, and will bring

you back to this land. I will not leave you till I shall have accomplished all that I have said."

Jacob awoke in the dawn. Glory rose in his throat like the bird song, glory and praise to the Lord.

"The Lord is in this place, and I knew it not," he whispered. "This is the house of God, and the gate of heaven."

Swiftly he took the stone, the rock that is today called Jacob's pillow, and set it up as a marker to God, Lord of the angels, Lord of Abraham and of Isaac, and now of Jacob.

And there in the sunrise Jacob swore to love God and serve Him forever. Never again would he harm that love by doing wrong.

Then he put his robe over the donkey's back for a saddle and traveled on toward Syria.

He took the same road as before, the rock-strewn, dusty hill path. The same road it was, but a different way. Now he was going to follow not his own will but God's will, and God's way.

The Dreamer

Where there are twelve brothers there is bound to be quarreling.

The family of Jacob, whose new name was Israel, was no exception.

One of the twelve, the boy named Joseph, was his father's favorite. That made most of the trouble. He was also a dreamer, which made matters worse.

His brothers—all except little Benjamin, who was still almost a baby—worked hard on their father's farm. They took care of thousands of sheep and cows and goats, leading them to far-off pastures. They were rugged, storm-bitten young men, used to battling wolves and robbers and weather.

"Joseph is a weakling!"

"And spoiled! What nonsense for Father to keep him home to study. Toughen him up, I say! He's not at all like us!"

That was true. Joseph did not seem strong. He was tall and slim, and graceful as a young tree that has not been gnarled by any wind. His mind was swift and keen as an eagle's flight.

He was clever with words and thoughts. Even as a boy he was wiser than many men.

And because he was young he did not know enough to hide his brilliance from his brothers. He showed off his cleverness. And they loathed him for it.

The most offensive thing about Joseph, however, was his dreaming. He was forever coming to table and saying:

"I had a dream last night that I sat on a great throne, and every one of you bowed down to me."

Or: "I dreamed that I was the lord of a kingdom, and you were beggars."

Jacob smiled at his son's stories because he loved him.

But his brothers despised him.

One fragrant spring day Jacob called Joseph from his studies.

"Your brothers have been gone a week to the far pastures. Go and see if all is well with them."

Joseph dressed himself in his dearest possession, his fine coat of many colors. Made of soft, strong wool, with long sleeves such as scholars wore, it was a gift from his father. Joseph did not dream how his brothers hated the sight of that rainbow coat!

From far off they heard him singing as he came, so full of himself in the elegant, gay, telltale coat.

"See—the dreamer comes!" said one, spitting on the ground.

"I'd like to kill him," muttered another.

The brothers looked at each other. Often before they had boasted of the terrible things they would like to do to Joseph. But now, as he came toward them, those empty threats suddenly became real, urgently important.

"Yes—let us kill him! The proud peacock!"

"Let us kill him and throw him in some pit. We'll say some evil beast devoured him."

"Then let us see what will become of his dreams!"

Only one spoke out for mercy to the huddled, bitter faces, the eldest brother, Reuben.

"Brothers—do not even speak of killing! You don't want the stain of murder on your head! Have you forgotten Cain, who killed his brother Abel?"

The others glared at Reuben.

"Throw him in a pit, if you must," said Reuben, "and leave him there to live or die. But do not kill him." Secretly Reuben planned to come back and rescue him from the pit.

Gaily smiling, all unsuspecting, Joseph came.

Three brothers seized him and forced him to the ground. They stripped off his fine coat, and stepped on it. Then with three more brothers helping, they lugged him off to a place not far from the highway and dropped him into a deep, dark pit.

"Now we shall see what becomes of your dreams!" Their laughter faded in the distance. Joseph was alone, shivering, bruised, and helpless.

Smugly Joseph's brothers sat on the grass to eat their lunch of bread and cheese. Then in the distance on the highway they could see a company of men coming. Ismaelites they were, foreigners, traders bringing dried fruits, sweet spices, and rare treasures to sell in the land of Egypt.

The strongest of the brothers, whose name was Judah, spoke:

"What good is it to let Joseph die? We could sell him to these merchants as a slave. Then we would be rid of him, and have a profit, too!"

To be sold into slavery? To be sold like an animal, belong to strangers and spend a whole life working as a prisoner?

"A fine idea!" said Joseph's brothers. At once they began arguing among themselves over the price they could get for him, and how to divide the money.

And while they argued, another band of strangers, wanderers from the land of Midian, happened along. The Midianites discovered Joseph in the pit. They saw that he was young and healthy, the kind of boy that would bring a good price as a slave. They saw too the camel caravan of Ismaelites. And while the brothers squabbled, the Midianites pulled Joseph out of the pit and sold him.

Twenty pieces of silver—about twelve dollars in American money—was the price the Midianites got for Joseph. And his brothers, of course, got nothing at all.

The Ismaelite caravan moved on, south to the mysterious sun-swept land of Egypt. Joseph, covered now in a ragged, dirty cloak, hands tied, walked along led by a rope like a donkey or an ox.

Once only he looked back. Over his shoulder Joseph saw his coat of many colors lying in the dust.

Later that same day his brothers picked up the coat.

"What will we tell Father about Joseph?" they had been asking. They had schemed and worried and fretted, terrified of Jacob's anger. After all, Jacob had once wrestled with an angel and won!

"Let him think Joseph is dead."

They took the coat of many colors. They killed a kid from the flock of goats, and dipped the coat in the blood. They smeared goat blood over it till it was stained a rusty red. And they brought it home and told Jacob that a wolf had eaten his favorite son.

Jacob tore his own clothes in grief. He wept until he had no more tears to shed.

When the camel train reached Egypt, Joseph was taken to the market place of the first town to be sold in an auction, where men could bid against each other to buy him.

A brawling, noisy place this market was. Drums were beating, bells ringing, as crowds jostled together, ready for anything. Here was an old woman selling melons, a man selling sweetened water from a gourd. Water buffalo for sale, gold bracelets for sale, purple cloths and leather sandals—and men for sale as slaves.

Joseph was put on a block of stone for all to see. Slave buyers looked him over, pinched him, measured him, peered at his teeth, felt of his muscles.

Then out of the crowd came one of the most important men in Egypt, an official named Potiphar. Potiphar was close to the man called Pharaoh, who was king of Egypt. And Potiphar needed a slave.

He bought Joseph. He took Joseph home and put him to work. At the beginning Joseph was given the dirtiest work of all, the scrubbing, the sweeping. But soon Potiphar could see that in Joseph he had a fine bargain. Joseph could read and write. Soon he learned to understand the strange language of the Egyptians. He outshone all the other slaves in willingness and intelligence, and always he was cheerful. Again and again Potiphar promoted Joseph. Ten years passed, and Joseph became the overseer of the whole house, the head of all the servants. He was almost as important as Potiphar himself.

But Potiphar's wife did not like this foreign slave. She was jealous because her husband would take Joseph's advice, and not hers. She wanted to be rid of him because he was the favorite—just as his brothers had wanted to be rid of him so long before.

So Potiphar's wife went to her husband and told a lie.

"This slave, called Joseph, attacked me. He spoke to me rudely. He insulted me. And—he struck me, and tore my clothes."

Potiphar believed her, of course. He turned on Joseph in anger and threw him in prison.

For the second time in ten years Joseph was a prisoner through no fault of his own.

Why?

Joseph sat in the darkest corner of the reeking, stinking jail. Ever since he was a little boy, he had loved God. His father Jacob had taught him to believe that God watched over those who loved Him and trusted Him. God had changed Jacob's name to Israel, and had chosen the children of Israel to belong to Him. But here in Egypt men had never heard of the God Who had spoken with Abraham, and Isaac, and Jacob. Here they prayed to grotesque statues of men with heads like those of birds and beasts. They even prayed to the sun up in the sky.

"My father said there was only one God," said Joseph. "Could it be that our God does not live in Egypt? Could He have forgotten me because I am here, and not in the land where He spoke to my fathers?"

Joseph did not understand the things that were happening to him. But even in this hour of disgrace and misery he decided to trust in the Lord.

And, as always, the moment that decision was made, God began to make the mystery clear.

Joseph resolved to make the best of his fate. He smiled. He

made friends with the other prisoners, the thieves, the robbers, the murderers, who were with him. So cheerful was he that even the keeper of the prison was charmed by him. Before long he put Joseph in charge of all the other prisoners. And as time passed Joseph realized with amazement that he was happy, even in the prison cell.

One dreary winter afternoon, as Joseph sat talking with his fellows, the prison doors swung open. With a rattle of chains, a clanging of thick leg irons, two men stumbled into the cell, as wretched a pair as one could find.

"Murderers! Dogs!"

With a mighty shove the keeper flung them at Joseph's feet.

"They tried to poison the mighty Pharaoh! This one was the chief butler. That one was the chief cook. They shall die a thousand deaths by slow torture."

Joseph welcomed them, and made them as comfortable as he could. Who was he to judge them? Who knew whether they were truly guilty? Not Joseph!

One morning, as Joseph rose with a smile from sleep, he found the butler and the cook trembling with fear.

"We have both had fearful dreams. Will you tell us what they mean? We have heard you are an expert in dreams."

"Tell me the dreams," said Joseph. "And God, Who knows all, may help us understand them."

God? The cook and the butler knew nothing of God. They knew only the strange gods of Egypt, the carved cats and bulls, the sphinxes and the sun and star gods that men had made. But still they asked Joseph to listen.

"I dreamed that I made wine from the grapes of a vine with three branches, and gave the wine to Pharaoh and he drank it," said the butler. "What can it mean?"

"It means that in three days Pharaoh will forgive you and

set you free," Joseph told the butler. "And when he does, remember me, and ask him to free me too!"

"I will! I will!" promised the butler.

Then the cook told his dream. "On my head were three white baskets of baked meats for Pharaoh. Birds came and ate all that was in the top basket. And I woke up terrified."

"In three days," said Joseph sadly, "you will be judged guilty, and hanged, and the birds will eat your flesh. That is the meaning of the dream God sent you."

Everything happened just as Joseph said. Three days later Pharaoh celebrated his birthday. He ordered the baker hanged from a tree. But the butler was freed, restored to his place in the palace for the royal birthday. And the butler was so happy he forgot all about Joseph.

Joseph must wait in prison. Two more long lonely years passed.

Then, suddenly, Pharaoh himself was troubled with dreams.

In his golden robes, pearl- and ruby-trimmed, Pharaoh walked the vaulted throne room in worried silence. His jeweled crown pressed heavily over his frown.

"Can no one tell me what these dreams mean?" roared Pharaoh. "Each night they come, the same dreams, haunting me. There is a secret to them, a message I cannot understand. Can no one tell me?"

Pharaoh's court was full of men who called themselves wise. His royal magicians and conjurers in robes of silver and black brewed strange potions and drank them, and spoke magic runes, but they could not understand the dreams. The royal astrologers searched the stars and found no answer. The royal wizards fingered the pale white sands in the mystic triangles they drew, and studied ancient charts, and knew nothing.

Night after night Pharaoh tossed in his sleep. In his cool bedchamber a perfumed fountain tinkled, and slave girls waved peacock plumes to fan his brow. His head lay on a silken pillow over a bolster of white alabaster. But always the dreams came to disturb him.

"I dream of seven fat cows, and seven scrawny, thin cows who come to eat them. I dream of seven full ears of corn, and seven thin and empty ears of corn that devour them. What can it mean?"

Finally the chief butler remembered Joseph, and, bowing low before Pharaoh, he told him of the foreign slave who could read dreams.

Pharaoh was desperate. Though his wizards and astrologers laughed, he sent for the prisoner.

Joseph stood before the gold and blue-enamel throne. He did not look impressive at all. He had no star-embroidered robe, no magic wand. He did not mutter strange rhymes or draw in the sand. He simply stood in his prison robe, and listened calmly to Pharaoh's dream. His head was bowed, and his eyes were closed, and he prayed while he listened.

"Why are you silent?" roared Pharaoh. "I have heard you are very wise in interpreting dreams."

Joseph opened his eyes. "It is not I, but God Who speaks in your dream. God has sent the dream to show you what He is about to do."

"Who is this God?"

"The one true God, Whom we, the Hebrews, the children of Israel know."

"Hmph!" said Pharaoh. "Well, what is this God going to do?"

"This is what your dream means," said Joseph. "For seven years there will be plenty in Egypt. Your harvests will be great, and there will be more food than you can eat. But then there will be seven years of famine, when no food will grow, and men will starve—unless something is done to make ready."

Pharaoh listened, and something about Joseph made him feel that indeed this God was speaking through him.

"Tell me, what must be done?"

"Pharaoh must choose a wise man and make him ruler over the land of Egypt. During the seven years of plenty this ruler must gather food into barns, and store it under Pharaoh's seal to save it for the years when no food grows."

Pharaoh smiled. "Can I find one wiser than you? You shall be the ruler. I shall sit on the throne. But you will be over all else, and all the people shall obey you."

And the king took a ring from his own hand and gave it to Joseph. He gave Joseph a robe of silk, though not of many colors, and hung a golden chain around his throat. Pharaoh made him governor, and gave him a beautiful wife. And then Pharaoh gave Joseph a new name, which was Egyptian, and meant in their language "Savior of the World."

Joseph now was thirty years old. And if he smiled strangely as he left the throne room, it was because he was beginning to appreciate God's plan. If his brothers had not wanted to kill him, if he had not been sold as a slave, if he had not been thrown into prison, he could not now be ruler of the mighty land of Egypt!

His smile deepened as he remembered the days when as a little boy he had told his own dreams to his brothers. They had laughed, then sneered at him. Even on that sad windy day when they had thrown him into the pit they had mocked him, saying:

"Let us see now what comes of his dreams!"

And what had he dreamed, that boy in the coat of many colors in the far-off land? He had dreamed that his brothers bowed before him, dreamed that he had been a king.

Indeed, he grinned, let us see what comes of my dreams— and of trusting God!

What Came of
Joseph's
Dreams

Joseph wore a golden crown, and robes of softest, tissue-thin cotton, and a golden chain.

Pharaoh, the great ruler of Egypt, had given Joseph his own signet ring, and a chariot second only to his own in magnificence, a palace, and a beautiful wife.

"I have everything the world can offer!" said Joseph, staring across the city at the pyramids far out on the sands. "Even two little boys of my own. And God has given me great work to do—for which I thank Him."

He strolled through the palace, past the rows of his servants, who greeted him in whispers, calling him by the new name Pharaoh had given him, which in Egyptian meant:

"Savior of the World!"

"Hail!"

He walked through the rows of date palms where his own tame gazelles played, and scarlet birds chattered.

"Yet I am lonely. No one here, not even my wife, speaks my own language, Hebrew. No one here has heard of the God of my fathers. Even I am beginning to look like an Egyptian, and speak as one. Will I never see my father again? Or my brothers?"

His brothers! Joseph grieved for them. Never had they given him as much as one kind word. They had ridiculed him, insulted him, threatened and attacked him, betrayed him. But Joseph did not hate them. His heart was full of the love of God, and he had no room for hate.

"Someday," he said, "I shall see them again. And when I do, what a strange time that will be for them—and for me!"

The day was coming, in God's secret swiftness.

Meanwhile Joseph was busy following out the meaning of Pharaoh's royal dreams.

Pharaoh, ruler of all Egypt, had dreamed, and God had helped Joseph understand those dreams: for seven years Egypt's farms would overflow with harvest, but then for seven years more famine would strike, and nothing would grow.

"I believe those dreams," the jeweled Pharaoh had said. "I appoint you, Joseph, my governor. During the years of plenty you shall gather food for the years of famine, so that Egypt shall not die of hunger."

Joseph did.

"Why should we listen to a foreigner, *a Hebrew*—and his God?" men said behind Pharaoh's back. "This is a hoax, a trick of some kind."

But surely the first part of Pharaoh's dream came true. For seven years the crops grew as never before, bursting, burgeoning with food. And Joseph built more and more storehouses to hoard the extra grain and rice and wheat. At his command Pharaoh's servants worked day and night, bundling and storing food, more food than anyone had ever seen.

And once more people laughed as they passed Joseph's palace:

"This foreigner, this Hebrew, is crazy!" men said. "There will never be a famine."

"We will never need all this food. Look how much grows now!"

The first seven years ended. The second seven began. And men no longer snickered at Joseph's gates.

Nothing grew. The river Nile failed, and shrank, and did not water the land. The sun shone with deadly heat, and no rain fell. Drought swept the country. The crops withered and died. There was no bread.

Then Joseph opened the storehouses, and sold food to everyone in Egypt, as Pharaoh, the king, commanded.

From the parched fields by the sphinxes of Luxor, from the deadened earth around the temples of the sun on the Upper Nile, from seaports and desert towns men came to the Governor for food. All Egypt was at his feet. And Joseph refused no one.

The famine spread like sickness across the earth, past the borders of Egypt to the countries all around. Travelers brought dismal tales of hungry men, and bone-thin animals. What little food the people of other lands had stored was soon gone. And they too came to Egypt, to Joseph, for bread.

To the north and east in the land of Canaan, once so green and lush with water, the grass withered, the sheep and goats sickened, and hunger prowled around the house where Jacob and his eleven other sons still lived.

"What shall we do? We will all starve!" the brothers said. "Our crops have failed. Our animals are dying of hunger."

"I have heard that wheat is sold in Egypt," said Jacob. "People say there is some magician there, a powerful governor, who has great storehouses. Go down to Egypt and buy us what we need to live. Only—leave Benjamin here. He is the youngest, and I want one son with me. Since Joseph was killed, I am afraid to let the young ones go from me."

And Jacob's eyes were wet with tears, as he thought of Joseph—eaten by a wild beast.

The ten brothers went to Egypt.

"Where may we buy wheat?"

"You must go to the Governor, and ask him."

"Who is this governor?"

"A friend of Pharaoh, a man with wondrous powers. We do not remember what his old name was," the Egyptians explained. "But our Pharaoh gave him a new name: Savior of the World. He is a terrifying person. Bow low before him and perhaps he will let you buy his food."

And so the stage was set for one of the strangest dramas in history.

The ten brothers went to the palace and bowed their heads to the floor, and they dared not look this powerful governor in the face.

From the carved glory of his throne Joseph glanced idly at the newcomers groveling at his feet. Then his hands gripped the sides of the chair as suddenly he recognized them. His face went pale. His heart thudded in his chest.

Swiftly he thought to himself: "They will never recognize me. Nearly twenty years have passed. The Egyptian sun has bronzed my face. I have an accent now—my voice is changed. I shall not tell them who I am. For a little while I will give them a hard time—let them remember the dreams they mocked!"

He spoke in a harsh voice:

"Foreigners! Where are you from?"

"From the land of Canaan. We came to buy what we need to live."

"Ah, no," said Joseph. "You did not come to buy. I think you are—spies!"

"No, my lord! We are your servants come to buy food. Peaceable men we are, and we do no evil."

"You are spies come to feel out the weakest parts of our land of Egypt!" roared Joseph.

"No, my lord," they said fearfully, their words tumbling over each other to explain. "We are the sons of one father. Ten of us are here. The youngest, Benjamin, is home with our father, Jacob, who is called Israel. And the other is dead—dead these many years. We are just family men, and we seek only food, for our family is starving."

Jacob, my father, is still alive! And Benjamin! Joseph's heart turned over with love and excitement. *I must find a way to see them! But if I tell my brothers who I am, they will be too ashamed and afraid to tell my father. I must trick them some more, and force them to bring Benjamin here. . . .*

"If what you say is true," said Joseph aloud, "then prove it to me. If you are not spies, then——"

"Yes?"

"Then one of you must stay here as a hostage, a prisoner while the rest of you go home and bring the other brother, the youngest one, here to me. If you bring him I shall believe you are not spies!"

Bring Benjamin here? Leave one of themselves as hostage? The brothers turned to each other in anguish. And they spoke among themselves in their own language, never dreaming that the Governor of Egypt could understand!

"We deserve to suffer these things because of what we did to our brother Joseph so long ago," said one.

"Didn't I tell you then not to hurt Joseph? And you didn't listen," said Reuben. "This is God's way of punishing us."

Joseph heard them, and tears came to his eyes, and he had to turn away so they could not see.

They chose to leave Brother Simeon behind. Joseph had him bound as a prisoner in front of the others.

"When you come with Benjamin, Simeon shall go free!" said Joseph. "Now I shall sell you some wheat to take home with you. Pay my steward, over there!"

The nine brothers paid. And Joseph gave secret orders to his servants who were to load up the brothers' sacks with grain.

"Fill each sack with wheat," said Joseph in a whisper. "And then . . ."

The brothers did not hear the rest. They took the sacks Joseph's men handed them, loaded them on their donkeys, and went their way, northward out of Egypt to their father's home.

And on the way they stopped at an inn. One brother opened his sack, to get grain to feed his donkey, and——

"Brothers—look! My money is back again! The same money I paid for this wheat is here in the bag!"

Each one looked in his sack. Each one found his money hidden there. Astonished, and a little worried, they scratched their beards.

"What a strange man this governor, this 'Savior of the World' is!"

Home again, they told their father Jacob everything that happened, ending with:

"We must bring Benjamin to Egypt."

"Never!" Jacob pounded his fist on the table. "You have

taken away all my children. Joseph is dead. Simeon is a prisoner in Egypt—and now you want to take Benjamin!"

The eldest brother, Reuben, said: "I promise to keep him safe."

But Jacob was firm. "Benjamin stays here."

In the meantime hunger still lay on the land. And the sacks of wheat from Egypt would not last forever.

When it was gone, Jacob said to his sons: "Go again and buy us a little food."

Judah, the strongest brother, said: "We told you what the Governor said. We must bring Benjamin. I promise to watch over him. No harm will come to him."

Jacob raised his eyes to heaven. "If it must be, it must be. But take with you presents for this mysterious governor—a little balm, and honey, and perfumes, and almonds. And take with you double money, in case the money you found in the sacks was a mistake. And may God bless you."

Once again the brothers bowed low before the Governor in Egypt.

With a catch in his throat Joseph saw that Benjamin was there, Benjamin, the one he loved best. Clapping his hands, he called his steward:

"Bring these men to my house, and prepare a feast! They shall eat with me at noon."

"What now?" the brothers whispered nervously as they went. "Could this be a trap?"

"Maybe he plans to accuse us of stealing the money that we found in our sacks. These Egyptians are strange people!"

"And what about Simeon? Where is he?"

Entering Joseph's house, the brothers found his steward.

"Sir!" they said. "We have come to return the money that——"

"What money? You owe nothing," smiled the steward. "And here—see, here is your brother."

Simeon, untied and unchained, hurried to greet them, but even he could not explain the mystery. So, while they waited for the Governor, the brothers began arranging the presents they had brought, and wondering what on earth this was all about.

Promptly at noon Joseph arrived in his gilded chariot. They rushed to offer him the gifts.

"Our father, Jacob, sent these."

Jacob, my father! Joseph yearned to see him! "How is he? Is he well?"

"Very well! And he sends you perfumed oils, and honey, and——"

"And this is Benjamin, the brother of whom you spoke?" Joseph turned to Benjamin. "May God be gracious to you," he said, and then he could say no more. The tears were ready to run down his cheeks at the sight of the brother he loved.

If the brothers were puzzled before, they were to become nearly desperate now!

After the feast, at which the Governor joined them, they set off for home again. Once more their sacks were filled with grain. But this time Joseph gave an even more mysterious order to his steward:

"Into each sack put the money they have paid, on top. But into the sack that is Benjamin's put my own silver cup. And tell no one!"

The brothers rode gaily out of the city. Joseph watched them go. And then, after an hour had passed, he said to his steward:

"Go after those men, and when you catch them ask them

why they have stolen my cup! And arrest them and bring them here."

The steward, who was also a very puzzled man, did as he was told. He caught the brothers, accused them, found the cup in Benjamin's sack, and brought them all back to Joseph.

"We are innocent!"

"Benjamin did not steal the cup!" cried Judah, the strongest brother, who had promised to take care of the boy.

"But how else did it get in his sack?" asked Joseph. "You may go free, all of you—but Benjamin must stay, and be my slave."

Judah groaned. "Our father Jacob loves him dearly. He will die of sorrow if we do not bring him home. Let me stay in his place, for I cannot return to my father without the boy, and see my father die of tears."

Joseph turned abruptly to his servants. "Leave us, all of you! Quickly—out of here! I must be alone with these men."

He buried his face in his hands till all of them were gone, and only the eleven brothers stood before him. Then, he rose and faced them with open arms.

"I am Joseph——" he began, and his voice broke into sobs.

"I am Joseph!"

The brothers stared at him as if he were a ghost, and they quaked with fear.

"Come nearer to me," he whispered.

They came.

"I am Joseph, your brother, whom you sold into Egypt. Don't be afraid, or think it was so terrible to do! It was God's will. He needed me here to prepare for the famine. He sent me here before you so that I could save you all when hunger came."

The brothers could not speak, could not move.

Joseph rushed on. "Go and tell my father, and bring him

here. God has made me lord of all Egypt. Bring my father and you can all live here. I'll give you a whole land to live in. And I'll give you food. And you shall be near me——"

But still they stood, frozen with fear and wonder.

"Look!" cried Joseph. "See my eyes—they are the same as yours. And see my mouth, listen—it is I, Joseph—your brother!"

And he hugged Benjamin to him and wept, and then he kissed each one of his brothers one after the other.

"You are Joseph!"

"And you kiss us?"

"Why not, Judah?" smiled Joseph through his tears. "You are my brother!"

Hours they spent together, talking. The brothers must tell Joseph all the news of home. And they listened as he told them the wonderful things that happened to him since the day they stripped his robe of many colors from him and flung him into the pit.

"You have even finer robes now, Joseph," said Benjamin.

"And this is what has become of your dreams," said Reuben. "I remember you dreamed you would be a mighty king, and that we would bow before you, and beg!"

Joseph smiled, and to each one he gave an Egyptian robe, heavy with jeweled embroidery—finer by far than the coat of many colors they had taken from him.

Eleven brothers hurried home.

"Father! Joseph—your son, Joseph—is not dead! He is living. And he is ruler of all the land of Egypt."

Old Jacob heard them and blinked, like someone waking out of a sound sleep.

"I do not believe you."

Carefully, slowly they told him the whole story. "And see —look what Joseph has sent you."

There before Jacob's house stood twenty asses, ten loaded with sacks of gold and silver and jewels and silken robes of the riches of Egypt. Ten more were loaded with food. And Jacob rubbed his eyes and said:

"If Joseph my son is living, I will go and see him before I die."

Jacob was more than a hundred years old. His beard reached to his knees. He walked with a limp. But he hurried like a boy to gather all his family—his sons and their wives who had always before stayed home, and their children —and his servants, and all his animals and everything he owned. And he started off to Egypt.

In the middle of the night, as Jacob slept in the camp, God spoke:

"I am the most mighty God. Fear not. Go down into Egypt, for I will make a great nation of you there."

Joseph rode out in his chariot to meet his father. And they fell on each other's necks and wept for joy.

And Pharaoh gave Jacob and his children the land of Gessen, or Goshen, in which to live, and keep their sheep.

And the family was together again.

"Father," said Joseph. "Is it not strange that both of us have had our names changed?"

"An angel of the Lord changed mine," said the old man. "He called me—Israel."

"And Pharaoh changed mine. He called me 'Savior of the World.'"

They were together—Israel, and the Savior of the World, for the first time, in Egypt.

When Jacob was one hundred and forty-seven years old, and knew he was about to die, he sent for Joseph, and Joseph's two Egyptian sons, Ephraim and Manasses.

"May the angel of God who has saved me from all evil bless these fine young men!"

Then Jacob called for all his own sons to circle his deathbed. One by one he blessed them, praising their virtues, and warning them of their faults.

"Listen, it is Israel, your father, who speaks!"

Blessings of Israel on the twelve tribes—on Reuben, Simeon, Levi, Judah, Zabulon, Issachar, Dan, Gad, Aser, Nephtali, Joseph and Benjamin. And for Joseph a special blessing:

"From Joseph's children's children shall come One Who will be the Shepherd, and the cornerstone of Israel."

Then Jacob sighed with weariness. "I must die," he said. "But bury me not in Egypt! Bury me in our own land, in the cave of Mambre. There my grandparents, Abraham and Sara lie, and my father and mother, Isaac and Rebecca, and my first wife Leah. My wife Rachel is buried in Bethlehem. But bury me with our people. . . ."

So Jacob, called Israel, died.

But the children of Israel, the twelve tribes, lived.

The Man
Who Spoke with
the Burning
Bush

In a small wattled mud house in Egypt lived a mother and three children, eight-year-old Miriam, three-year-old Aaron, and a new baby with soft fuzzy hair.

The baby was hidden. His mother had wrapped him in cloths, and put him behind a table, in a cradle of hay, where he could not be seen.

He was hidden because his mother did not want him to die.

"Every boy baby that is born to an Israelite family must be killed!" The gold-crowned Pharaoh, ruler of all Egypt, had given that order. And every day soldiers tramped through the lanes of little houses, with murder in their curved swords.

"I don't understand, Mother," said black-haired Miriam. "Why does the Pharaoh hate our people?"

"For many reasons, child. He hates us because we are foreigners. Our people came to Egypt hundreds of years ago, and the man who was Pharaoh then loved our father Israel, and his son Joseph. So that Pharaoh told us to live in this place, the land of Goshen, and made us welcome. But time has passed and this Pharaoh is different."

"Why else, Mother?" asked Miriam, helping to form the loaves of bread.

"Because we have grown strong, and great in numbers, and a little wealthy, I suppose. But I think the real reason is our God. Pharaoh worships many strange and foolish gods—the ones whose statues you have seen. He is afraid of us because we believe in the only one true God. He wants to destroy us, to crush us forever. That is why he has made our men slaves. And why he kills our baby boys."

Miriam shivered.

"Do not be afraid, my child. The Lord God will save us. Of that I am sure."

Just then the baby behind the table cried. His little heels thudded against the wall.

"Miriam," said the mother. "We cannot keep him here much longer. He is three months old, and soon someone is bound to find him. I have a plan. Perhaps we can save him, still."

With papyrus reeds and hot sticky pitch the mother and Miriam made a small waterproof basket, a floating cradle. They put the baby in it, and carried it to the river Nile, and launched it in the tall grass and bulrushes in the shallows of the river.

The mother prayed her child would be safe. But before the prayer was finished, she began to cry, and she ran away, home to little Aaron. She did not know that Miriam still waited and watched by the river as the gentle waters rocked the strange boat.

Suddenly the sound of women's voices, laughing and talking, came close to the river. Lovely Princess Bithia, the daughter of Pharaoh, came to wash herself, attended by her maids.

Bithia stood not ten feet from the basket. Miriam held her breath.

And then the baby cried.

Pharaoh's daughter found him in the bulrushes. She picked him up and looked at him, and then held him close to her.

"It is a Hebrew baby, an Israelite, whose mother is trying to save him!" Tears rolled down her own face at the thought.

"He shall be mine!" she said. "I shall keep him. And I shall call him—Moses."

Little did she know that the child she had rescued would be known by the whole world, and that the name she gave him would be famous forever!

Out of the tangled reeds appeared a pale and watchful little girl, her eyes bright with a secret, daring plan.

Miriam bowed before the princess.

"Does the noble lady wish me to bring her a Hebrew nurse for this child?" Miriam asked. "I know where there is one."

The princess looked at her thoughtfully. "Do so," she said. "Bring her to nurse the child, and I will pay her wages."

Pharaoh's daughter defied her own father's commands to rescue a despised Hebrew baby from death. She hired a nurse for him. And she did not know that the nurse little Miriam brought was the baby's own mother!

Year after year, as Moses grew, his real mother took care of him. She taught him to walk, to talk both Egyptian and Hebrew, and to know the one true God Whom the Israelites knew.

The princess, on the other hand, raised him as part of the royal court. This Israelite boy wore the robes of a prince. He studied under tutors, and at the university in the Temple of Egypt. He had his own servants, and his own animals, and fine gold chains to wear.

As Moses grew older, he was unhappy in the palace. His own people, the Israelites, were poor miserable slaves, forced to work to make the rich men of Egypt even richer. And these men in the palace thought of their slaves as no more than animals!

Moses would slip quietly out of the palace, to wander in the places where his kinsmen were working. By the river the Pharaoh was planning a new series of mighty dams. The Hebrew slaves were building them under the blazing sun.

A few steps away from Moses a Hebrew slave fell exhausted on the sand. An Egyptian overseer's whip cracked across the man's naked back.

Anger burst inside Moses. Leaping upon the overseer, Moses broke the Egyptian's neck.

Then, seeing no one around, Moses hid the body in the sand.

The next day he went again to the building crews by the river. This time he found two Hebrews fighting together, and one was whipping the other. Bravely Moses stepped between them.

"Why are you striking your own kinsman?"

The guilty one pushed his chin boldly into Moses' face. "Who made you our ruler and our judge? Do you plan to kill me—as you killed the Egyptian?"

Moses stepped back, his face pale. His bloody deed was known? He must flee, at once, before Pharaoh learned of it and ordered him put to death!

Moses hurried for his life, east across the desert to the land of Midian, at the head of the Red Sea.

Years passed. Moses found a home with a holy man named Jethro. He married one of Jethro's seven beautiful daughters, a girl called Sepphora. He worked as a shepherd, tending Jethro's flocks.

From time to time travelers brought news of Egypt. Pharaoh Seti I died, and the new Pharaoh, Rameses II, rose to the throne, and he was even more cruel than the others. Still the Israelites suffered in slavery, and cried out to God to deliver them.

In Midian, Moses prayed, and wondered when, if ever, God would rescue his people. He would lead Jethro's sheep through rich green pastures and bare bleak deserts, even to the rocky reaches of the sky-piercing mountain called Horeb, or Sinai.

Moses shielded his eyes as he stared up at the mountain.

The peaks thrilled him. It seemed somehow as if the mountain could be the very home of the Lord God!

One afternoon, as he tended the sheep on the lower slopes, Moses prayed as usual for peace, and for justice for his people. He was thinking of his mother, perhaps dead by now, of his sister Miriam, and his brother Aaron, whom he had not seen in years. . . .

Then a remarkable thing happened.

Suddenly before his eyes a thornbush burst into flame. The fire burned bright and red in the midst of the bush, but—here was the strange thing—not one twig crumpled, or charred. It was burning, but it was not burned!

Moses took a step forward. From the burning bush a voice called out to him, a voice not of this earth:

"Moses! Come no closer! You are standing on holy ground!"

It was the Voice of God. The Voice that spoke in Eden to Adam and Eve and the serpent, and to Noah the ark builder, to Abraham, Isaac, and Jacob, now rose clearly from the burning bush.

Moses covered his face in fear and trembling.

"I have seen how My people suffer in Egypt," said the Lord. "I have come to rescue them from the Egyptians and lead them to a land flowing with milk and honey. I will send you, Moses, to Pharaoh, to lead My people, the children of Israel, out of Egypt!"

Moses' hands fell to his sides.

"Who am I to go to Pharaoh—and lead the Israelites out of Egypt?"

"I will be with you," said the Voice.

"But suppose I say to them: 'The God of your fathers has sent me.' And suppose they ask: 'What is His name?' What shall I say?"

The Voice replied:

"I Am Who Am."

And then He also said, "Say to the children of Israel: 'He Who Is, sent me to you.'"

So it was that the Lord God came to be called Yahweh (sometimes Jehovah)—*I Am Who Am*—which means that God is the One Who was in the beginning, is now, and ever shall be, and Who makes everything else that is.

Now God told Moses what to do.

Moses must return to Egypt, gather the elders of Israel together, and go with them to Pharaoh to ask him to let the Israelites go.

"But I know," said the Lord Yahweh, "that Pharaoh will not let you go unless he is forced. He will refuse, and I will stretch out My hand and strike Egypt with all My wonders. After these he will let you go!"

Moses listened. He trusted God. But all at once the job seemed too big, too terrifying for him. He did not trust himself!

"Who will listen to me?" asked Moses. "Who will believe that God spoke—*to me?*"

"What is that in your hand?" asked God.

"A staff—a shepherd's stick."

"Throw it down on the ground!"

Moses obeyed. The staff struck the ground and instantly it became a living serpent.

"Now put out your hand and take it by the tail!"

Moses did. In his hand it became again the familiar weathered-brown stick.

"This will be a sign so that all may believe that the Lord, the God of their fathers, did appear to you!"

Two other signs God gave Moses.

He told Moses to put his hand inside his cloak. When Moses brought his hand out again it was white with the sores of leprosy. When again he put his hand inside and drew it out, the hand was healed.

"And," said the Lord, "if they still will not believe you, take water from the river and pour it on the land. The water will become blood."

Moses knew such wonders would astound the people and make them listen to him. But he knew too that he must speak well when they did listen or else he might fail the Lord.

"Please, Lord. I have never been a fine speaker. I am slow of speech!"

"Who makes one man speak, and another man deaf and dumb?" thundered the Voice from the bush. "Is it not I, the Lord? Go! I will be with your mouth, and teach you what you are to say."

Still Moses hung back.

"If You please, Lord, send someone else!"

Then the Lord grew angry with Moses, and said, "Aaron, your brother, is an eloquent speaker. He is now coming to meet you, and together you will speak what I will teach you to say. He shall speak to the people for you."

Then, before Moses could again object, the Voice left one last flaming command:

"Take this staff in your hand. With it you shall work the wonders and the signs!"

The fire faded and was gone.

The thorn bush, no longer flaming, all green and bright, unsinged, moved gently in the gloaming wind. The solemn silence ended. Now Moses heard again the familiar sounds, buzz of insects, birdcalls, and the bleating of lambs.

Moses held his staff in his hands and faced Egypt. The love of the Lord burned in his heart, as indestructible and bright as it had blazed in the bush.

The Night
Death
Passed Over

Two brothers stood in the court of Pharaoh Rameses II.

Pharaoh sat on a golden-lion throne, his slim body covered with jewels, surrounded by slaves waving palm fans, and soldiers with shields and helmets. Gaudily robed wizards and magicians sniffed into scarlet kerchiefs and peered down their noses.

Moses, in the brown robes of a shepherd, stood beside Aaron. They had no weapons, except their plain wooden staffs. They had no armor except their faith in God.

"Two Israelites—here in the court? Israelites are slaves—worthless people!" muttered the royal wizards.

"How dare they come here?" whispered the guards.

Pharaoh himself stared with eyes of stone at the two white-bearded shepherds.

"Speak!" he commanded in a voice sharp as a whip.

Aaron spoke for Moses, as he was always to do. "Our God, the Lord God of Israel, has spoken," said Aaron. The courtiers smiled. They did not believe in the Lord whether He spoke or kept silent.

"The Lord has said that Pharaoh must let His people go, that they may celebrate a feast for Him in the desert," said Aaron.

Let the Israelites go? Rameses' lips curled. His scornful laughter rang out through the columned court. The Israelites were the finest army of slaves a king could find. They worked hard, for nothing. Rameses had them carving mammoth statues of himself, and building giant temples to Egyptian gods along the waters of the Nile.

"Who is this Lord that I should obey Him?" sneered Pharaoh. "I do not know Him! And I will not let Israel go!"

Moses whispered in his brother's ear, and Aaron spoke for him.

"Let our people go a three-days' journey into the desert to make sacrifices to our God. Otherwise—the God of the Hebrews will send terrible pestilences and troubles—and death —to Egypt!"

Pharaoh sprang from his throne. Fury flashed in his eyes. How dare these wretched brothers threaten him with such talk! "Get you gone!" thundered Pharaoh.

And, to be certain that never again would a Hebrew, or an Israelite, be so bold, Pharaoh issued new and cruel orders to make life harder for the slaves.

The Israelites had been forced to make bricks for Pharaoh's buildings, bricks formed from half-dried clay mixed with straw. Always Pharaoh's men had provided the straw for the bricks.

Now Pharaoh called his overseers and taskmasters:

"Give no more straw to these people, but let them go and gather straw themselves. They are lazy and idle! That is why they listen to these lying words about the Lord, and sacrifice in some desert! Make them gather their own straw, and tell them they must work harder, for they must produce as many bricks each day as before!"

Straw did not grow near the brickworks. The Israelites had to search all over Egypt, scrabbling in fields far away, to find straw, and bring it back before they could begin to make bricks. Even with women and children helping, they could not make as many as before.

"You have not made enough!" The whips of the taskmasters cracked over the backs of the slaves.

Then, exactly as Pharaoh had hoped, the Israelites turned against the two men who could save them. They went to Moses and Aaron, and shook their fists in their faces, and cried:

"Look what you have done by going to Pharaoh! Now things are worse than ever for us. Leave us alone, and let us simply obey Pharaoh and be slaves!"

Moses watched them leave, and his heart was sad and torn with puzzlement. The Lord Himself had spoken to him from a burning bush, and given him these orders. He was only obeying God. Why, then, did he seem to fail so miserably?

"Lord," he prayed, "why did You let more trouble afflict Your people? Since I went to Pharaoh in Your name he has oppressed and tormented Your people—and You did not deliver them!"

Out of the stillness spoke the Voice:

"Tell the children of Israel: I am the Lord, and I will take you to Me, and I will be your God. I will bring you out of Egypt into the land which I promised to give to Abraham, to Isaac and to Jacob."

And what about Pharaoh?

"His heart shall be hardened," said the Lord, "for he is proud, and stubborn, and filled with malice. I will work many signs and wonders in Egypt, and still he will not hear you.

And I will stretch out My hand over Egypt, and lead the Israelites out of the land, so that the Egyptians may learn that I am the Lord!"

Then began a battle of wonders, a series of signs, each ordered by God, and carefully performed by Moses and Aaron, a siege of miracles against Pharaoh's hard heart.

The Lord said: "When Pharaoh asks you for a miracle to prove that I am God, let Aaron throw his staff upon the ground, and it shall become a serpent."

Back to the carved throne room went Moses and Aaron. Aaron threw his staff upon the marble floor. Instantly it became a snake.

Pharaoh raised one eyebrow, and with a crook of his finger called his own magicians and wizards. In gilded robes and strange, figured hats they advanced toward the brothers. Then each one in turn threw his own staff upon the ground.

Cackling with smug, victorious laughter, they pointed. Their staffs too had become serpents!

Suddenly the sniggering laughter stopped. The rod-serpent of Moses and Aaron swallowed all of the others right before their eyes. Aaron reached down and took his serpent by its tail. Immediately it became, again, a plain wooden staff.

Pharaoh watched. His lips twitched, but he said nothing. He rose from the throne, and swept silently from the room.

Next morning Pharaoh and his courtiers went down to the river Nile to bathe. In leisurely magnificence they walked, with silken umbrellas, and music, and waving fans. They had deliberately forgotten about the unpleasant nuisance of Moses and his God, and the promises of pestilence and troubles.

They could not forget for long. At the water's edge, near

the bulrushes where he had floated as a baby, stood Moses with Aaron, and the miraculous staff.

"Pharaoh!" called Moses. "The Lord God of the Hebrews sent me to you, and you did not listen!"

Pharaoh shrugged his slim shoulders, and waved a ruby-ringed hand as if to brush Moses away like a fly.

Moses did not budge. "Here, then, O mighty Pharaoh, is a sign ordered by the Lord. The waters of Egypt shall change —to blood!"

At Moses' word Aaron raised the staff over the blue-brown waters of the Nile.

It changed to blood. Pharaoh saw it. It turned red, and thick, and stinking. Fish died and floated to the surface.

At the same instant the waters of every stream and pool and canal, even the water in jugs or in stone jars in the houses, turned to blood all over Egypt.

Pharaoh gasped. He raised a vial of perfume to his nose and turned away from the filthy river, and went home to his palace.

No water? He would drink the juice of oranges, the light wines of the East, the milk of goats. The people could dig new wells, or wait for rain, or do without water. It was no matter to trouble a pharaoh!

"This blood-water cannot last forever," said Pharaoh. He was right. It lasted seven days, and then the water cleared.

But the Lord had more business with Pharaoh.

Once more Moses stood before him.

"If you do not let the people go to worship the Lord, He will strike your land with—frogs!"

Frogs? Pharaoh laughed out loud. What could be terrible about frogs?

Aaron raised the staff again over the waters of Egypt. From the riverbanks came the green hopping army, croaking and lunging, millions upon millions of frogs, more than man had ever seen.

Frogs covered the outdoors, the fields, the roads, the streets till no one could move without stepping on one. Frogs covered the yards, stables, and barns. Frogs entered the houses, squawked through the bedrooms and kitchens, into the ovens, into the storerooms, into the refuse, into the throne room itself!

Pharaoh sent for Moses. He did not like these signs. He did not like the frogs. He was surly and sulky as a child.

"Pray to your Lord to remove these frogs," said Pharaoh, "and then I will let your people go worship in the desert."

Moses did not believe him, but he acted as if he did, giving him the benefit of the doubt. Perhaps, thought Moses, another miracle would convince Pharaoh for good.

"Set a time," said Moses, "and at that particular time I will pray for this plague to end."

"Tomorrow!" said Pharaoh as the frogs swarmed around his throne.

"You shall see there is none as powerful as the Lord, our God."

The next day Moses prayed, and while he prayed the plague ended.

Frogs hurried desperately toward the river. Those that failed fell dead where they were. Millions of frogs lay dead, to be gathered into stinking heaps and burned. The only ones left alive were in the river and ponds, where frogs belong.

Pharaoh drew a sigh of relief, and broke his word. He refused to let the Israelites go. He laughed in Moses' face. He saw no need to be grateful to the Lord.

Then the Lord said to Moses and Aaron: "Stretch out your staff and strike the dust of Egypt that it may become—gnats!"

The dust turned to gnats. The dust rose and the air filled

with uncountable hordes of insects, tormenting and biting the people.

In the palace royal wizards and magicians tried to banish the gnats, and they could not. They struck the dust with magic wands, and they could not do what Aaron had done. Finally even they said:

"This is the work of God!"

But Pharaoh did not listen.

Next day Moses and Aaron again demanded that Pharaoh release the people. Again he refused.

Suddenly the sky blackened and the wind hummed with the buzz of a tremendous swarm of flies. Biting flies covered all of Egypt, crawling on the faces of the Egyptians, getting into their eyes and ears and mouths. But there were no flies in the land of Goshen, where the Israelites lived!

"I will let you go into the desert to sacrifice to your God," said Pharaoh, "if you do not go too far away, and if you will pray for me."

"I will pray that tomorrow the Lord will take away the flies."

But, when the flies vanished the next day, Pharaoh changed his mind. He would not let the people go.

Day after day the Lord hurled new plagues on Egypt. Each time Pharaoh would promise to obey the Lord, and each time he broke his word.

Pestilence came on the farm animals, a pestilence on all horses, donkeys, camels, cows, pigs, and sheep. The animals of the Egyptians sickened and died. The Israelites' animals stayed sleek and healthy.

A plague of boils descended. Red festering sores burst out on the bodies of every Egyptian, so painful that no one at all came to the throne room, not even Pharaoh.

As usual Pharaoh begged Moses to remove the plague, and when the boils vanished he refused to let the Hebrews go.

Again the blue skies darkened. A storm of intense violence crashed upon the earth. Hailstones, wind, thunder, and lightning splintered stately palm trees and battered men and beasts, crushing the flax and barley fields. But in the land of Goshen, where the Israelites were, the sun shone.

Pharaoh begged Moses to pray. The hail stopped. But Pharaoh did not let the people go.

"Behold," said Moses calmly, "the Lord tomorrow will bring in a plague of locusts to cover the face of the earth."

Pharaoh's own servants and courtiers pleaded with him not to offend the Lord God of Israel more, and to let the people go, but Pharaoh refused.

That same night a burning wind blew over Egypt. At dawn the wind brought the locusts, long, fat, hungry insects, buzzing and droning and clacking their wings in big brown clouds. They covered the land, and ate every living thing the hail had spared, till not a leaf or a blade of grass remained. They tumbled through windows and doors and filled the houses of the poor and the palaces of Pharaoh.

"Pray to your God!" cried Pharaoh. Moses prayed. A strong wind rose in the west and blew the locusts away. But Pharaoh, after eight plagues, and eight promises, was still stubborn. He took back his promise.

The next morning the land of Egypt was dark. There was no dawn. The Lord sent a darkness so thick it could almost be touched. In the land of Goshen the sun shone, but in the rest of Egypt for three days no one saw sunrise or moonrise, only impenetrable dark. People stayed in their beds, afraid to move.

With burning torches Pharaoh's messengers went to bring Moses and Aaron to the court.

"Go, worship the Lord!" sighed Pharaoh. "You may all go, young and old, women and children too. I will not change my mind again. Only—your flocks of sheep and cattle must stay behind."

"No," said Moses. "We need our animals to make sacrifices and burn offerings. We must bring them all."

"I shall refuse!" roared Pharaoh.

"Then," replied Moses solemnly, "listen to what I say. The Lord God will take the first-born of the Egyptians, and the first-born of all their beasts, and they shall die overnight."

The eldest son in every house in the land? And the first offspring of every sheep and cow and horse? No plague could be worse than that!

"There will be loud weeping in Egypt," said Moses sadly. "Then, you will beg us to leave your land."

Pharaoh snorted with rage, and swallowed his fear. "Get out! And never come to me again, or *you* shall die!"

Moses bowed. "Indeed," he said, "I will never come to see you again."

Moses and Aaron rushed back to the land of Goshen and the elders of Israel. The Lord had carefully instructed Moses. Much must be done—and quickly! The night is coming when the Lord will free His people, and lead them out of Egypt!

Each Israelite family must be warned, and prepared for immediate departure. Not only must women pack, and men prepare the herds, but there is a special dinner to be prepared, a ritual to be performed, a sign of Israel's love and honor for the Lord.

This is the night of the first feast of Passover—the night when God's anger will pass over the houses of Israel, and strike only at His enemies.

Quickly but carefully Moses explained, repeating the orders God had given him.

This night, the fourteenth of the springtime month which today is called April but was then called Abib, and later Nisan, would never be forgotten in the history of Israel.

Each family must pick a perfect one-year-old male lamb from its flocks, and kill it, as if it were a sacrifice to God. Then the blood of the lamb must be sprinkled on the lintel and doorposts of the house. The blood of the lamb would save Israel from the wrath of the Lord.

"No one shall go out of his house till morning," ordered Moses. "This night the Lord will come to strike death to the Egyptians. When He sees the blood, the Lord will pass over that door, and the destroyer shall not come in!"

One more command. The lamb must be roasted, and eaten with unleavened bread and bitter herbs, and every morsel must be consumed, eaten or burned. Each family must eat dressed for the journey, with shoes on, and the traveler's staff in hand.

The dinners were prepared. The men of Israel dipped hyssop branches in lamb's blood and marked their doors. Families in traveling cloaks ate together the meal of lamb and wild bitters and flat, unleavened wafers of bread. And as they ate they trembled in awe at the mysteries of the Lord.

Precisely at midnight death came.

Death rushed through the land, silent and swift and chill.

In every Egyptian family the eldest boy fell dead. The eldest son of rich and poor, from the lowliest hovel to Pharaoh's palace, withered suddenly and died, alive one instant, gone the next.

"Let the children of Israel go!" the cry rose. "Let them go!"

The weeping of fathers and mothers echoed in the dark. Pharaoh himself was weeping over his own dead son. The guards, the wizards, the servants, the taskmasters, each had lost someone. Out in the fields and barns the first-born of each cow and sheep fell dead.

Without waiting for dawn Pharaoh called Moses and Aaron. "Go away from my people, you and the children of Israel—go. Take your sheep, and your herds, and go!"

The hullabaloo was fantastic in the darkness, the hurry and noise and confusion as the children of Israel began to leave.

They were a family, the grandsons and great-great-grandsons of one man, but four hundred and thirty years had passed since old Jacob, whose name became Israel, first came to Egypt. The family now numbered six hundred thousand men, not counting children. The family, the twelve tribes, had become a nation! It was the largest caravan anyone ever saw, with cattle and sheep complaining loudly, and little dogs yapping, and babies crying, and over it all the glorious singing of the people whom the Lord had saved.

This was the first Passover, the day of gladness and triumph.

By God's orders, year after year, the children of Israel would keep this holy day. They would dedicate their firstborn sons to the Lord, to be redeemed from Him by the blood of a lamb. And each year they would meet in holy ritual to eat the lamb.

Dawn shattered the darkness of Egypt, spilling golden glory across the walls where Israelites had worked in slavery. Singing and dancing, they marched toward the desert.

With plagues and death the Lord had driven the Egyptians to their knees. He was leading His people to the Promised Land.

The Mystery
of the
Red Sea

The little boy's feet sank into the sands of the desert as he hurried along beside his father.

The boy did not go far from his side because in such a crowd it was easy to get lost. Six hundred thousand men, not counting the women and children—nearly a million people altogether—trudged through the yellow dust. On their backs, in their arms, in saddlebags on donkeys they were carrying pots, jugs, tools, food, clothes, toys, blankets, everything they owned.

"Where are we going?" the boy asked. He was still sleepy. The family had left home before dawn.

"Out of Egypt," said his father. "We will be slaves of Pharaoh no more."

"But *where* are we going?"

"To the Promised Land!"

The boy blinked the dust out of his eyes, shifted his pack from the left arm to the right, and thought back to what he knew about the Promised Land. His mother and father had been careful to teach him all about the Lord God. He knew about Adam and Eve, and Noah, and Abraham. And he remembered that hundreds upon hundreds of years before the Lord had promised Abraham, and Abraham's descendants, their own land, rich and green and fertile.

"Is the Lord Himself leading us?" asked the boy.

"He is," said his father. "The Lord has chosen a man named Moses, the big-shouldered one with the white beard. . . ."

That first day the desert winds danced with the sound of laughter and singing and the high spirit of adventure. The boy ran beside the herds of sheep and of cows. He wandered in and out of the columns of happy people. At night they made camp on the desert sands under the stars, snuggled close around in families.

When the boy woke the next morning he knew something was wrong.

The men were not singing as they began to march. Dark scowls covered their faces, and the boy began to feel afraid. He walked closer to the other groups, listening, and he heard men muttering:

"The Promised Land is to the north, and we are going south—into the worst part of the desert!"

"We were fools to come after an old man with his talk about the Lord! What does Moses know of the desert?"

The boy slipped back beside his father.

"We're going the wrong way," said the boy. "We're lost, and we are all going to die in the desert. I am scared!"

The father dug his staff into the sand and wiped his forehead and bent down beside the boy.

"You have listened to men," he said. "But only God can know what is right for us. The greatest lesson a boy can learn is to trust God, and trust Him when it is hardest of all to do!"

The boy nodded. "But how do you know whether God is really leading you?"

"You have to decide whether to believe," said his father. "And usually, once you have decided, then God will show you!"

The sun grew hotter, burning, blinding, searing-hot. The night was bitter cold, as often is true in a desert. In the darkness blew the icy wind of the Sarsar, freezing to the bone. The Promised Land seemed very far away.

"There are no signposts in the desert, no paths, no roads. But anyone can see by the sun and stars that we are going the exact opposite direction from the Promised Land!"

"Are you sure you know where you lead us, Moses?"

Men clustered around Moses with angry eyes. They pushed their faces close to his.

Moses knew where he was going because the Lord had spoken to him. He knew that the Lord was leading them a longer way, in a great semicircle, because on the shorter route armed bandits lay in wait, and fierce warriors.

But Moses also knew that God does not always explain His reasons to each of His followers. Like some children who insist on asking more questions instead of doing what they are told, the people must learn to trust the Lord!

Moses stood calmly in front of the angry men. He had never asked to be a leader. He did not want to be one. He was simply obeying the Lord, Who had first spoken to him from the burning bush and Who had been giving him strange but wise commands ever since.

"Answer us!" they shouted, brandishing their staffs in his face.

Moses could see the thousands of others strung out in a caravan across the desert, waiting patiently, trusting him and the Lord. Silently he prayed.

Suddenly a gasp like a great wind ran through the caravan. "Look!"

There before them all, at the precise head of the line of march, stood a giant pillar of cloud!

Tall as heaven, wide as an army walking abreast, towered a column of pure white cloud. And it did not stand still. Silently, solidly, slowly it moved forward.

"It is the Lord showing us the way!"

It was, indeed, the Lord. The pillar of cloud glided forward. The people shouldered their packs, picked up their babies, goaded their flocks, and followed in a strange parade.

They whispered in wonder at sight of the cloud, but as afternoon died and night came, a shout of amazement rose from their throats.

The pillar of cloud became in the darkness a pillar of fire!

It led them through the night to a campsite in the shifting sands and stopped and stood guard over them, a shining plume of blazing light. In the morning it became cloud again. Serenely, surely it moved ahead, and the people of Israel followed.

"Thank the Lord!" said the people.

And those who had doubted the loudest said to each other solemnly: "You see, we should always trust God, and not ourselves!"

They did not complain any more, at least for a few days.

The pillar of cloud and fire led them toward the mysterious, whispering waters of the Red Sea, which is between what we call Arabia and Egypt. Purposefully, busily the cloud led them across miles of flat, bare sand toward the water. There, in midday, it stopped.

The Israelites stopped too, and made camp. The women began to think of chores to be done, of dusty clothes to wash, and bread to bake. Children swarmed on the shore, kicking blistered heels in the sea, and building sand castles dampened with the warm salt water.

But many of the men stood squinting at the sea, and talking, and their words were ominous and dark with worry.

"We can't stay here! We're not safe—we're still in Egypt!"

"Pharaoh never did want to let us go. He needs slaves. He could capture us here, or slaughter us if we tried to fight."

"This is the narrowest part of the sea, but still it's more than a mile across. And we have no boats!"

Soon nearly everyone was sitting on the sand staring at the sea and worrying.

The boy climbed on his father's lap. "Did you not say the Lord would take care of us?"

"I did."

"But, Father—look!" The boy pointed back to the west, toward Egypt.

Dust swirled in the distance. Men rose to their feet to look. Sunlight gleamed on sharp shafts of metal in the dust—spears! Far across the flat wastes of the desert horse-drawn chariots thundered toward them. It was the army of Pharaoh!

Terrible fear flared among the Israelites, wild-voiced terror. They screamed out to God to help them, and did not stop to listen if He answered. Mothers swooped down on their children, and hugged them to them. Men with clenched fists and desperate voices stampeded toward Moses.

"Why did you make us leave Egypt? Are we to die in the desert like dogs? Better to be a live slave in Egypt than to die here!"

Moses raised his large, gaunt hands for silence. For a long moment he looked with sad, dark eyes at these people who still had so little faith. These people had been chosen by the Lord. For them the Lord had worked miracles in Egypt. He had freed them, even led them with fire and cloud. Yet in each new danger they forgot how powerful the Lord was!

The chariot thunder came clearly on the desert wind, but Moses' voice rang deep.

"Fear not!" he said. "The Lord will win your victory."

His long, bony finger pointed to the sky.

Slowly the people turned to see where he pointed, westward to the desert where the enemy chariots rolled. They could still hear them. But they could not see them!

While they had been screaming at Moses, the Lord's pillar of cloud had moved, and settled itself down between them and the Egyptians, a wall to hide them from view. The sudden night of the desert swept over the land, but for this once the pillar did not turn to fire. It held the enemy in utter darkness.

The people nudged each other, and whispered in amazement, but Moses had received a new secret command from the Lord.

He took his staff in his hand, the same wondrous stick that had become a snake before Pharaoh's eyes, the same staff that had turned the waters of Egypt to blood. He raised the staff now over the restless waters of the Red Sea.

A rushing sound like wingbeats filled the air.

An east wind sprang down from heaven. The wind blew upon the waters. It furrowed them and harrowed them and pushed them, and separated them. The waters parted! As the wind blew and the night grew old, the waters stood like two giant walls and in between was dry land—a road across the sea.

Silently the pillar of cloud slid through the night, taking its place once more at the head of the caravan. And, when it reached the edge of the sea, it blazed again in fire!

"Forward!"

One by one, hundreds by hundreds, thousands upon thousands, the Israelites rushed through the parted sea. On either side of them the waters stood like mountains, miraculously held up by the wind. Far over their heads the water towered, wondrous, sullen, liquid piles of mystery. The pillar of fire moved swiftly ahead, lighting the way. And children, hurrying across the sea, bent down to rescue strange shells from the earth which the Lord had made dry for them.

Across the desert the Egyptians awoke. When the pillar of cloud had blocked the Israelites from view, the Egyptians had made camp in the desert, leaving only a few on watch. Now soldiers and officers scrambled to their feet, helmets and breastplates rattling loud in the chill dawn. Horses whinnied and neighed at the weird sight of fire and mountainous water. The Egyptians leaped into their chariots, raised their spears, whipped their steeds, and screamed for battle.

Those chariots were built for speed. They traveled much faster than families plodding with children and animals and sacks of household goods. The chariots rushed toward the sea, faster, faster—then lurchingly, joltingly they suddenly stopped.

From the pillar of fire a strange ray pierced the darkness. Instantly the chariot wheels had slowed. Drivers shouted, officers roared. The wheels clogged and caught.

"This God of Israel, this God of the Hebrews, is too strong!" cried the soldiers. "Let us turn back."

"Turn back and you die!" With spears and drawn swords the officers ordered them on.

The Israelites were almost across the sea.

With balky wheels the Egyptians clanged and clacked after them. Now they could see the marvelous walls of water. Horses shied and backed away from entering the road through the sea, but the Egyptians pressed on. Soon the whole

Egyptian Army, the six hundred first-class chariots and all the other chariots, was in the middle of the divided sea.

The last Israelite family reached the opposite shore, where Moses stood listening to the secret word of the Lord.

Moses raised his rod. The walls of water shuddered and trembled, and tumbled, and collapsed. Ton upon ton of water crashed over the Egyptians, foaming, churning, drenching, crushing, and closed over them, swallowing them as if they had never been.

Waves clashed high, and swelled, and settled, and swelled again.

Holding each other close, the Israelites stood on the shore and watched, and there were no words to speak of the awful power of the Lord. The rising sun painted the water crests in palest gold, and a gentle breeze blew in the hair of the people. The only sound was the sound of the mysterious waters of the sea.

Then gently, firmly came the voice of Moses:

> "I will sing to the Lord, for He has triumphed.
> "The horse and the rider He has cast into the sea.
> "My strength and my courage is the Lord . . .
> "He is my God and I praise Him."

Moses' voice rose as he sang, and the men joined him in the dawnlight, singing glory to their God. And Moses' sister Miriam took a timbrel in her hand, a tambourine, and began to dance in praise of the Lord, and the other women took up theirs and followed her in a dance of joy.

The boy put his hand in his father's, and knew that the Lord will indeed protect His own. He will snatch them from the jaws of danger, and guard them with a mighty hand.

The Ten Commandments

The mountain was steep and desolate and bleak that day as Moses, alone, struggled upward. Below lay the desert of Sinai, and the vast row of tents where Israel camped.

Up, up the white-bearded leader was climbing, hurrying breathlessly back to the spot where once he had seen a bush burn without being destroyed. What God had promised that day—what had then seemed impossible—was done! The children of Israel were no longer slaves in Egypt. The Lord had set them free, and had led them out of Egypt.

An eagle took wing, flapping her wings against the sun and wind, as Moses pushed on higher. Then, when he could stagger only a few steps more, he heard the Voice:

"Moses! Moses!"

"Here am I, Lord," gasped Moses.

"This is what you shall say to Israel: 'You have seen what I did to the Egyptians, and how I raised you from danger as if on eagles' wings, and brought you here to Myself. Now, therefore, if you will obey Me, and keep My laws, then you shall be to Me, above all people, a peculiar treasure. And you shall be to Me a kingdom of priests and a holy nation.' That is what you shall say to the children of Israel."

The Voice ended. Moses knew he would hear no more that day. Raising himself from the stony ground, Moses gazed at the sky, and the words rang in his ears, the promise of God to the people of Israel:

". . . you shall be to Me, above all people, a peculiar treasure . . . a holy nation . . ."

Once again in camp he immediately called a meeting of the elders. To these, the wisest and most respected of the men of Israel, he gave the tremendous message of God.

"Why did the Lord choose us?"

"Are we strong enough to bear such a burden? Look how often our people grumbled and complained and doubted the Lord already!"

"Why did He choose us?"

Moses could not answer the questions. All he could do was hold fast to his faith. The Lord had spoken. He believed the Lord and trusted Him.

The trumpet sounded at daybreak next morning, calling the people from their tents. To them all Moses repeated God's words. A shout rose as from one throat:

"We will do all that the Lord asks!"

Moses beamed with pride and joy. "Blessed be the name of the Lord," he said, and climbed the mountain again to report to the Lord what the people had said.

The Lord answered:

"I shall come to you in a thick cloud, so the people may hear Me speak with you, and believe you, and obey you without question from now on."

To Moses God explained what the people must do to make ready for this. "They must sanctify themselves. They must make themselves clean, their bodies, their clothes, and their thoughts. On the third day the Lord will appear. But you must not let any of the people come too close to the mountain, or go up on it, or even touch it. Anyone who touches the mountain must be killed!"

On the morning of the third day all the people of Israel, clean in body and heart, gathered around the mountain at a careful distance from the boundary lines Moses had made.

Lightning split the sky. Thunder seemed to tumble from heaven. The earth shook while cattle and sheep lurched across the meadows. A heavy cloud settled over the mountain, and the top of the mountain blazed with fire. Black smoke bellowed over the great rocks and filled the deep ravines.

The Lord had come in majesty and power that the hardest heart must recognize and know!

Then God spoke, and the words He spoke that day from the holy mountain are known the world over. They were what we call today the Ten Commandments, the unbreakable laws of God.

"I am the Lord, your God!" The Voice seemed to come from the thunder and fire, from the sky above and the earth below. "You shall have no other gods. You shall not carve for yourselves idols in the shape of anything in the sky or on the earth, or under the earth. You shall not bow down before any other gods made by men."

That was the first commandment, the great truth on which the whole world is built, that there is only one God, Who is the Lord. We must obey Him, and honor Him. We must believe in Him, and trust in Him, and love Him above all things. And we must never think that any other power is greater than God, Who made all things.

Then the Lord said:

"You shall not take the name of the Lord your God in vain."

And by that second commandment the Lord meant that no one must use His holy name in anger, or in a slighting manner, or curse or wish people evil in His name, or speak or think insults against God.

Then the Lord said:

"Remember that you keep holy the Sabbath day! Six days shall you labor and do all your work, but the seventh day is the Sabbath of the Lord, and no work may be done . . . for in six days the Lord made heaven and earth, the sea, and all that is in them, but on the seventh day He rested. Therefore the Lord has blessed the Sabbath day and made it holy."

Then the Lord said:

"Honor your father and your mother!"

And by that commandment the Lord blessed the family and explained to all the world the special importance of parents. Next to God stand the mother and father, because they work with God to raise His children, and keep them safe in body and soul. Because of this, children owe to parents love, honor, and obedience, even when it is difficult to give. To those who keep this commandment God promised a long life and a happy one.

Then the Lord said:

"You shall not kill!"

And by that command He meant not only that a man may not actually take the life of another, but that no one may do anything to injure another or himself in body or soul. It is a command against anger, and quarreling, envy, hatred, or giving bad examples, and encouraging others to do wrong. For there is a kind of death in everything that is wrong.

Then the Lord said:

"You shall not commit adultery!"

And He meant that husbands and wives must love each

other and be faithful to each other, and that children must be modest, and pure in heart, remembering that all love is a holy and beautiful thing.

The Lord said:

"You shall not steal!"

And He meant not only that we may not take things that are not ours. He also meant that we may not cheat, or neglect to pay what we owe or borrow, or keep lost things from their real owners, or be unfair in any way.

The Lord said:

"You shall not bear false witness against your neighbor!"

And He meant that we may not tell lies at any time, for any reason. And by the same commandment He meant that we may not be talebearers, or gossips, or hypocrites, or use our tongues for anything but honest and kind words.

"You shall not covet your neighbor's wife," said the Lord.

"You shall not covet your neighbor's house, nor his servants, nor his goods, nor anything that is your neighbor's!"

And He meant that we should not be jealous of what anyone else has, but be glad with what God has given us, and content.

Those were the Ten Commandments, the ten laws which God gave to the people of Israel, and to us, from the mountain.

"There is nothing new in most of these commandments," said one man quietly. "They are common sense. If those laws were broken, the world would fall apart."

In a way that was true. They were the laws any reasonable man could see were needed if people were to live together in peace. They must honor and love their God. They must keep their families strong and close. They must be able to trust each other, and do nothing to hurt each other.

But in another way these laws were different from any

other laws in the world, because they were spoken by God. For the first time God told people exactly what He expected from them. To break these laws was a sin. To obey was to be a friend of God!

The thunders rolled and the lightnings flashed. Smoke poured from the holy mountain, and strange trumpets blasted. The people were afraid. They pushed each other slowly backward, away from the mountain. They called out to Moses:

"You speak to us, and we will listen to you. But we are afraid of the Voice of God Himself!"

Moses called through the thunder. "Do not be afraid! God has come in thunder and lightning to show you His power, and to give you a holy fear of Him so you will not sin!"

Still the people backed away, so Moses went for them, closer to the cloud on the mountain. Then the Lord, speaking to Moses, gave many more laws for His people. Some were detailed rules of justice for all kinds of wrongdoing. Some were about the way to build an altar for the Lord. And many were warnings about the future.

These people were, after all, on their way to the Promised Land, and the angel of the Lord was to lead them. But, on the way they would meet many other peoples who did not believe in the Lord. They would find men who prayed before fierce stone idols, and offered weird sacrifices to pagan gods. The people of Israel must be careful not to fall into the traps of sin that lay between them and the Promised Land.

Moses came slowly down from the mountain, his heart full of thoughts that surged and rolled like the sea.

The Lord has called us out of slavery, and saved us, and chosen us as His own, thought Moses. *Ahead, somewhere, lies the Promised Land. The way before us is long and danger-*

ous. Armed enemies lie in wait. But if we walk according to the law of the Lord, we will reach the Promised Land!

And, thought Moses, *that is probably true of each one of us personally, as well as of all the people of Israel!*

Moses told the people everything the Lord had said.

"The Lord is making a covenant with you, an agreement and a promise. If you keep His laws, He will make you His own people, a holy people!"

They answered in a ringing voice that echoed across the plains:

"We will do everything the Lord has commanded!"

So Moses spent the night in his tent writing down everything the Lord had told him on a long scroll of parchment, which is what people then used for books.

Early in the morning Moses called the strongest young men and showed them how to build an altar for the Lord at the bottom of the mountain, and he had them build twelve pillars near the altar, one for each of the tribes of Israel.

Then Moses sent other young men to pick out the finest young bulls to offer as sacrifices to the Lord. The blood of the bulls he put into large bowls. Half the blood he put on the altar. Then he took the Book of the Covenant and read it aloud for the people, the Ten Commandments and all, so that they would remember exactly what they had promised to do. Then he took the rest of the blood of the sacrifice and sprinkled it on the people, saying:

"This is the blood of the Covenant, which the Lord has made with you!"

The people had promised to obey the Lord. He had promised to make them His own. And the promise was sealed with blood.

Then Moses and his brother Aaron, and Aaron's sons Nadab and Abiu, and seventy of the wise old men of Israel went up the mountain again, and they all saw the Lord, radiant and shining, with the sapphire-blue sky under His feet.

The others were not allowed to come close. But the Lord called Moses and said:

"Come up higher on the mountain with Me, and I will give you the stone tablets on which I have written the ten commandments."

After Moses went up, a cloud of glory covered the mountain. To the people below it seemed that the Lord was a fire on the mountain, but Moses went into the cloud and stayed there forty days and forty nights.

The Wonderful
Story
of Joshua

Moses was dead. The new leader of Israel was the warrior
Joshua, a man of courage and wisdom, and fiery, deep, dark
eyes.

"Prepare to cross the Jordan into the Promised Land," said
the Lord to Joshua. "Know no fear, for the Lord your God is
with you!"

The task ahead of Joshua was tremendous. He was to lead
his army of desert-wandering people into one of the most
heavily fortified countries in the world. He was to conquer
the land of Canaan and destroy every living man, woman,
and child in it. The Lord had promised the land to Israel, but
they must do battle to take it.

Joshua stood beside the swollen torrents of the river Jordan,
rushing and flooding with the spring rains. Across the river
was Jericho, first city to be seen in Canaan.

"The land is beautiful and rich. That we know," said
Joshua. "And we know that their cities are walled like fortresses, and their kings ride to battle in terrible iron char-

iots. But how strong are they? How ready are they to fight? These things we must know."

Joshua chose two trusted soldiers to cross the Jordan and scout. Unseen, the two spies slipped through the thronged gates of Jericho. Once past the walls, they went to the first inn they saw, a busy place run by a woman named Rahab. They hoped to eavesdrop on the talk in the dining room, and learn what the men of Jericho were thinking about war.

They were not so clever as they thought. They were seen, and recognized as spies by Rahab, and by others. Rahab laughed and sang as usual with her customers at their food and drink, pretending not to notice them because she thought it wise not to meddle with problems of war. But others were not as discreet. Word flew to the palace itself. By nightfall soldiers of the king were pounding on the inn door.

"Rahab! The king commands you to hand over the two strangers in your house. They are spies!"

Rahab peered through the doorway, a yellow shawl drawn under her pitch-black curls. From a high window she had seen the soldiers coming. Now her golden earrings jangled as she tossed her head.

"I never dreamed they were spies!" she said. "I didn't know where they came from. But they are gone. At twilight, when it was time to close the town gate, they left. I don't know where they went, but you must go after them immediately for they have a long head start!"

The soldiers thanked her and hurried toward the river. The mighty fortress gate opened for them, and closed fast behind them.

Then Rahab climbed narrow, winding stairs to the roof. There, as always in early spring, she had stalks of flax spread to dry, making them ready for spinning into linen. Rahab moved quietly through the moonless night. Carefully she lifted the tallest stalks of flax.

"Make no noise!" she whispered hoarsely. "The soldiers are gone. You are safe for a while."

The two spies brushed the warm, damp wisps of flax from their robes.

"You hid us, and saved us—why?"

Rahab sat on the roof beside them, her bracelets tinkling. "I know that your God has promised you this land. We all know it, and we are afraid. We have heard of the miracles the Lord has worked for you, and how He wins your battles. I can see that the Lord your God is God in heaven above and on earth below."

She bent her head close to them, and the richness of her perfume made their heads swim.

"A bargain!" she said. "I was good to you, and helped you. Now, swear to me by your God that you will save me, and my family, when you conquer Jericho!"

"You saved our lives—we will save yours!"

Rahab led them down into the house, to a window facing outside the rugged city wall. With a thick rope she lowered them to the ground.

"How shall I know I will be safe?" Her raucous whisper grated through the cloudy night.

"Take the scarlet sash from your dress. Tie it in this same window!"

As they vanished into the night, Rahab took off her scarlet sash and tied it in the window.

The spies reported to Joshua, "The people in Jericho are in deadly fear of us. It is time to attack."

Joshua nodded, and went to pray. He knew that no victory could be won without the help of God. And that night the Lord gave him the orders for battle, the strangest instructions any captain ever received. Only a man who trusted God completely, only a man full of obedience, could have accepted such advice. Joshua followed what he heard to the letter.

First the army must cross the river Jordan, now raging over its bank. There were no bridges. The fords were flooded.

Officers throughout the camp repeated Joshua's orders. "When you see the priests carry the holy Ark of the Covenant, break camp and follow wherever it goes."

The priests carrying the Ark stopped at the edge of the foaming green waters of the Jordan, paused a moment, and stepped into the river. They waded in. Instantly the water stopped flowing. An invisible dam held the river back, piling the upstream waters high in a solid mass. The downstream waters rushed onward toward the Dead Sea till they vanished.

To Joshua the Lord had said: "This day I will show Israel that I will work as great wonders through you as I did through Moses."

The people followed Joshua across the dry land where the river had flowed, exactly as their fathers had followed Moses across the Red Sea. The priests holding the Ark of the Covenant stood in the river bed until the whole nation crossed. When the last one of all the thousands reached the other side, the priests marched forward.

Their feet touched the shore. The piled-up waters collapsed behind them, splashing and thundering, racing onward to the Dead Sea.

Israel had reached the Promised Land! They were in Canaan at last, and they sang and danced and offered thanks to the mighty Lord, their God.

"We are here in Canaan, Joshua. We must march immediately to capture the cities!"

Joshua shook his head. That was not the Lord's plan. The

invading army crossed the borders of the country and stopped, to camp for two weeks without moving.

"I don't understand!" said a young captain to Joshua.

"If we do not understand, God does. That is enough."

"But the kings of this country will fall on us here and destroy us."

"They will not," said Joshua. And they did not. The kings of the country had heard how the Jordan waters dried up for Israel, and they were afraid. And Israel camped on the plains before Jericho, and prayed, and celebrated the feast of Passover as God had commanded.

All this time, for forty years, the Israelites had eaten manna, the bread which fell from heaven. On the day after Passover, as the Lord commanded, they ate unleavened bread made from the grain growing in the Promised Land. That same day the manna did not fall. It never came again.

"Why no more manna, Joshua? What is wrong?"

"You are in the Promised Land. The manna was food for the journey. The journey is over!"

Joshua was waiting for God's command. He walked alone on the plains in sight of the mighty walled city of Jericho. Suddenly his way was barred by a figure with a drawn sword.

"Friend or foe?" cried Joshua.

"I am the captain of the army of the Lord!" replied the angel.

And the angel told Joshua exactly what must be done to conquer Jericho.

Obedient as always, Joshua gave his orders in the morning. He ordered seven priests to march in front of the other priests who were to carry the Ark of the Covenant. Ahead of them would march the elite troops of Israel. And behind them were to walk all the other people. There was to be no noise, no talking, no shouting. The only sound was to be the blast of the ram's-horns blown by the first seven priests.

"Where do we march, Joshua?"

"Around the city. Once."

That morning the strange procession marched once around the city and returned to camp. The next morning they did the same thing. They did the same thing once each day for six days.

"This is insane!" the soldiers muttered. "What kind of man is Joshua to think of this?"

Joshua did not think of it. The Lord had commanded it. Joshua obeyed.

On the sixth night he called the people together. "The Lord has ordered us tomorrow to march around the city seven times. And then when the ram's-horns give a long blast, all the people must shout aloud. Then, says the Lord, the walls will fall to the ground, and Jericho will be ours."

The people stared at each other in amazement.

"But," said Joshua, "do not forget the Lord's laws about the looting of conquered cities. You must take nothing for yourselves. Every living thing in the city must be destroyed. And the gold and silver, must go to the treasury of the Lord!"

Seven times Joshua led them around the city of Jericho. Then the priests blew furiously on the curved ram's-horns. And the people opened their mouths and shouted, the wildest, loudest shout in the world.

The walls came tumbling down.

They cracked and shuddered and crumbled, not because of the shout, not because of the march, but because of the power of God, and the faith of people who obeyed Him.

Through the rumbling dust Joshua called his two spies. "Run to the house of Rahab, where the scarlet sash hangs, and bring her and her family safely here, as you swore to do."

The armies of Israel marched over the shattered walls into the city of Jericho, and killed all the men and women and animals in it, as the Lord commanded. But Rahab and her entire family were welcomed into the camp of Israel because she had saved the lives of the two men whom Joshua had sent.

And as the years passed, dark-curled Rahab married a fine man of the tribe of Judah, handsome young Salmon. And, strangely enough, as St. Matthew's Gospel relates, Rahab became the great-great-grandmother of King David, from whose family came Joseph, the carpenter of Nazareth, and Mary, the mother of Jesus.

Joshua and the people of Israel could not stop at Jericho. They must conquer the whole land of Canaan.

"Who can be afraid? We cannot lose a battle with the Lord our God to help us!"

"So long as we keep His laws, He will be with us," said Joshua. "But if even the smallest law is broken, He will forsake us."

Near Jericho stood a smaller walled town called Hai. Joshua sent three thousand of his men to capture Hai, certain that they would win with no trouble. But that night Joshua's army limped back to him, completely defeated!

"What happened? The enemy were few!"

No one answered. The soldiers were too ashamed, too terrified. Had the Lord deserted them?

Joshua and the elders of Israel prayed before the Ark of the Covenant. "Lord," cried Joshua, "why did You allow this to happen? What can I say when the Israelites are defeated, and run away from the enemy?"

And the Voice of the Lord replied: "Israel has sinned. One of you has broken My law, and stolen goods from Jericho and

hidden them. I will not remain with you while My law is broken."

Early the next morning Joshua held court in Jericho, an investigation which came down to one guilty-faced soldier named Achan.

"I did it," said Achan. "I saw the silver, I saw the gold, and I saw a magnificent shawl. I knew they belonged to the Lord, and I took them, and buried them inside my tent."

One man out of thousands, one sin—but where all men are together before God one man's sin blackens all. Achan was executed according to the law. The gold and silver and the mantle were delivered to the treasury of the house of the Lord.

Then God spoke again to Joshua. "Now be not afraid, but lead your army against Hai. Set an ambush, and you shall win."

Half his army Joshua sent secretly around behind the city. The other half he led to the front gates. The men of Hai came out to battle the front force, and Joshua made his troops seem to run away again in defeat. The men of Hai roared out in pursuit, leaving their city unguarded. Then the rest of Joshua's army, in ambush behind the city, rushed in, and captured it. The men of Hai were defeated, their city burned to the ground.

By now the whole country had heard of Joshua and the army of Israel. The six kings of the west met together in an alliance to battle against Joshua. But the king of Gabaon had a different plan. He did not think anyone could battle with the God of Israel and win. So he came up with an unusual scheme.

He sent an embassy to Joshua. The men who were to go were dressed in worn-out shoes and old, patched clothes.

They packed their donkeys with very old wineskins, and all the bread they took was moldy and crumbly.

They came to Joshua and said:

"We have come from a very far land to ask you to make an alliance with us. We want to make a treaty of peace."

Joshua had orders to destroy all the people who now lived in the Promised Land. He said cautiously: "If you are living in the land promised to us, we cannot make an alliance with you."

"We come from a long way off," they said. "We heard of the fame of the Lord, your God, and our people sent us to make an alliance. Look—this bread was fresh from the oven when we left, now it is dry and old. Our wineskins were new, now they're worthless. Our clothes and our shoes are worn out from our long travels!"

Joshua believed them. He made an alliance with them, and swore he would never do battle with them.

It was only three days later that Joshua, leading his army down the road, came to the city of Gabaon, and saw the same people who had said they lived so far away!

"We have sworn not to harm them!" cried the people. "But look! They are living in the Promised Land!"

"Why did you lie to us?" Joshua thundered.

"We knew that God had given you the land, and that all its people were to be destroyed and we were afraid. What will you do with us?"

Joshua had promised in the name of God. He did not harm the men of Gabaon, but let them live, as servants for Israel. But the troubles of the Gabaonites were not over. The king of Jerusalem and the other kings of the mountains heard what Gabaon had done, and marched against the city, laying siege to it.

"Come and help us!" The men of Gabaon sent word to Joshua.

Through the whole night Joshua's armies marched from Galgal to Gabaon, where the five kings camped in siege.

"There are five armies against you, Joshua!"

Joshua smiled, and his answer rang back across the ranks of the soldiers of Israel. "The Lord has said, 'Fear not!' "

Before the five kings dreamed they were near, Joshua's army fell on them in the dawnlight. The enemies fought with short, sharp spears and spiked war clubs, and broadswords. Blood spilled on the fields under the burning sun. Joshua's men fought bravely, but the enemy was fierce. This was to be no easy victory!

Hour after hour they fought, javelins hurtling through the air, spears clanging on shields, swords slashing. And as they fought the five kings began to realize that something was strange beyond words.

"How long have we fought?"

"Hour after hour!"

"But look at the sun!"

The sun stood still in the sky over Gabaon.

"Look, there—in the valley of Ajalon—the moon stands still!"

A stranger day has never been, before or since. The sun stood still in the sky, and not for a whole day did time move on. It was impossible, a thing that could not happen, but happen it did, when Joshua prayed.

Sunset was delayed, and the night did not come. There was nowhere and no time for the armies of the five kings to rest. And Joshua who had many fresh, untired reserves, kept replacing his soldiers with new relays. The armies of the five kings were massacred as Joshua stood tall and bronzed by the sun, on the hilltop over the fields.

The five kings ran for their lives, and hid in a damp, bat-flown cave. But Joshua found them, and captured them, and hanged them on five trees.

Battle followed battle, victory after victory. Thirty-one kings fell before Joshua and his warriors, until the whole land of Canaan was theirs, and Joshua was very old.

When the fighting was done, Joshua divided up the land as Moses had said, among the tribes of Israel. And then at the city of Shiloh, in a wide valley not far from Jerusalem, the people set up the Tabernacle for the Lord, where He would dwell among them forever.

At last Israel was at rest in the Promised Land. The years of wandering in the desert, of homelessness and hunger and thirst, of bloodshed and battle seemed very far away.

Joshua knew the end of his life was near. Like Moses, he loved these people, and yearned over them like a father, praying that they would stay close to the way of God. He called their leaders to him in the place called Sichem and spoke to them. He reminded them of all that God had done for them since the days of Abraham.

And Joshua said:

"Choose this day whom you shall serve. There are many false gods in this world, imaginary powers, and idols, as you have seen in Egypt, even as Abraham's fathers knew in Babylon. Whom will you serve—false gods, or the Lord?"

The people chanted:

"We will never forsake the Lord our God!"

Joshua warned them:

"It is not easy to serve the Lord! If after all He has done you forsake Him and bow before the false gods of the people around you, He will destroy you!"

"We will serve the Lord!" they cried. "We will obey His voice."

Joshua had served God all the one hundred and ten years of his life. He had led the armies of Israel into battle. He had been the shepherd who led the flock of Israel into the Promised Land. And like a captain giving final orders, like a shepherd checking the fold, he had done his best with his last breath to keep the soul of Israel close to God.

Joshua, valiant servant of the Lord, was dead.

The Strongest
Man
in the World

"These are terrible times we live in," said the farmer as he sat by his wife under the sunset.

"The Lord has abandoned Israel," she said. "The people turned away from the Lord, and He has left us in misery."

"Even the Judges, the men chosen by God, have failed us," said the farmer, whose name was Manue. "The last good one was Gideon, who had seventy sons. After he died, one of his sons, Abimelech, murdered all his brothers except one, Joatham, who escaped. And Abimelech made himself king, and ruined Israel with his cruel ways. He killed more than two thousand of his own people—burned them alive, because they dared to defy him. Then he was killed, and a good day that was."

His wife nodded. "Then came Thola, and then Jair, and they were good. They kept Israel close to the Lord. But when they died, the men of Israel went back to worshiping that hideous idol Baal, and so the Lord, as always, let Israel be conquered again!"

"Then there was Jephta, who rescued us for a while, and Abesan, and Ahialon and Abdon. But now Abdon's been dead these forty years, and the altars of the Lord are dusty and crumbling. The people worship false gods, and the mighty Philistines have us at their mercy."

"I pray that the Lord will send us a leader!" sighed his wife.

"Nearly a hundred years have passed since Gideon," said Manue sadly. "I fear the Lord has justly forgotten Israel."

"Still, we must pray," said his wife. And, as always, God listens to the prayers of those who love Him.

Two nights later the woman was alone in her room when suddenly an angel appeared to her.

"Poor woman," said the angel. "The Lord knows how you have prayed. He knows too that all your life you have wanted a baby and had none. Now you will bear a child, a son, who is to be dedicated to God. And he shall strike down the Philistines and free Israel."

As the woman listened, the angel explained one curious rule.

"You are to taste no wine and no unclean food. And your son shall be what is called a Nazerite, which means that to show his holiness for God he must never cut his hair, not even as a child. He must belong to God."

Tears of joy streaming down her face, she ran to tell Manue the wondrous news. And the angel appeared again to both of them out in the fields and repeated his message.

"What is your name?" cried Manue.

"Do not ask my name," said the angel. "It is too great and mysterious for men to know."

Manue prepared a sacrifice for the Lord on a rock in the fields. The flames of burnt offering soared up to heaven, and the angel vanished upward along the tongues of fire.

And in time a son was born to Manue and his wife, a boy with long black hair whom they named Samson.

From the beginning his parents could see that this child was like no other. His strength was amazing. When he took his first steps the ground seemed to shake. He played with boulders the way others played with pebbles. He carried a calf on his back when he was only three, and lifted a bull over a fence when he was nine.

"This strength is what will save Israel," said Manue proudly.

"But this strength is dangerous, too," said Samson's mother. She tried to teach her boy to cling close to God's law, because she knew that the power that made him great could ruin him if it were not used properly.

She watched Samson grow from a boy into a man, saw his thick black hair fall below his shoulders, and she worried over him. He was a Judge in Israel, as the Lord had chosen him. People brought their problems to him to decide, and he judged them wisely and well. He worshiped the Lord and led the people back to the Lord. But by himself he was not a very serious man.

"It is not good to use your strength as a toy, Samson," his mother would say. "What God gives you should be used for His service."

Samson laughed. "The girls like to see me so strong," he said.

That was the danger for Samson. His mother knew it. His father Manue knew it. There are some young men who are so vain that all they can think of is having lovely girls sighing over them. Manue was afraid that Samson would even forget his Lord for the sake of a pretty face.

"Why do you not marry, my son?" asked Manue.

"I will," said Samson. "I have found the girl I want most.

She is a Philistine woman, from the town of Thamnatha. I beg you—get her for my wife."

"A Philistine girl? Is there no one of our own people whom you love? Why must you marry an enemy, a girl who does not even believe in the Lord? Is this any way for a Judge of Israel to act?"

Manue and his wife did not know that it was the Lord's will that Samson choose a Philistine girl. They often wondered exactly when and how He would send Samson against the Philistines. They could not have guessed that this was His way.

Samson pleaded with them, and begged them, and insisted. Finally Manue and his wife agreed to go to the father and mother of the girl and arrange the marriage, which was the custom in those days.

Samson went with them down to Thamnatha, but as usual he did not walk beside them. He ranged afield, making side trips into hills and valleys, testing his strength in the trunks of trees, or the mountain boulders.

Just outside the town, as Samson clumped his way through a vineyard, danger stared him in the eye. A lion leaped for his throat, roaring, raging, jaws wide for the kill.

Samson caught him in mid-air. His giant hands closed around the lion's neck. He strangled the lion, crushed it to death, and then tore it apart as a man might tear a cooked chicken. He left the pieces on the ground, washed the blood off his hands, and caught up with his parents.

Arrangements for the marriage were quickly made. The Philistines were delighted to have such a fine, strong son-in-law. Samson and his parents went home to prepare clothes and gifts and all that was necessary. Soon they were again on the way to Thamnatha, ready for the wedding.

On the way Samson remembered the lion. He had never

told his parents about it. It was odd the way he felt about his strength. He had never let anyone know how strong he really was. Even the little feats he performed so effortlessly seemed marvelous to other people. He kept the greater things—like tearing the lion apart—to himself.

He found the lion's carcass picked clean by the crows and buzzards. But inside the skull, where the mouth had been, a swarm of bees had made a honeycomb. Brushing the bees aside, Samson took the honey in his fists and ate it.

But he told no one.

At the Philistine's house crowds of guests awaited the bridegroom. The wedding service took only a few minutes. The wedding feast was to take seven days!

Samson was almost a stranger here. The only person he knew well was his bride. And he did not feel at all at home, even though the Philistines gave him thirty young men as companions for the feast, to serve as best man at the wedding and male attendants. Samson was used to simple life, to farm dinners, and village folk dances. These Philistines were more sophisticated. They drank great goblets of wine, and made strange jokes, and sang songs and told stories Samson could not understand.

Slowly Samson began to realize that behind their hands they were laughing at him. They did not like him. They looked at him as a country bumpkin, a curiosity who was amusing because he was big and strong and had such unusually long black hair.

Samson sat drinking fruit juice and milk and wondering while the godless Philistines caroused with wine and coarse laughter. He looked at his bride and consoled himself. At least, he thought, she loves me. She would not marry me if she thought the way they do. And Samson decided it was time he tried to take part in the fun. He was not a good

dancer. He could not sing. But one of the games these Philistine men enjoyed most was riddles. They would pose conundrums for each other and make bets as to who could guess them. Samson thought, and finally he said to his thirty Philistine companions:

"I have a riddle for you. And if you can guess it before the seven days of the marriage feast are over, I will give you each a new suit of clothes. But if you can't guess it, you must give me thirty suits of clothes."

"Oho!" they laughed. "The farmer's son has a riddle? An Israelite gives a Philistine a riddle? Let's hear it!"

Samson said: "Out of the eater came food. Out of the strong came sweetness."

The Philistines tried to solve that riddle. They came up with all kinds of answers, but not one was right. And as the days and nights passed, they grew desperate. Thirty suits of clothes was a large bet to lose! But worse than that would be the blow to their pride if they lost.

Finally they went to Samson's wife. "You must find out from Samson what the answer is!" they said. "We will be ruined if we do not answer. And—if you don't, we'll burn down your father's house, and you in it."

Samson's wife was not brave enough to face that threat! She put her arms around Samson's neck, and said: "Samson, dearest. I don't think you love me. If you loved me you would tell me the answer to the riddle."

He laughed. "I didn't tell my own father and mother!"

But she did not stop pestering him. Day and night she asked him. She teased him, and kissed him, and she even cried, till finally on the last day of the feast he was so tired of her asking that he told her about the lion, and the honey he found in the skull. And she, of course, hurried to tell the young men.

Samson sat at the feast table watching the dancers. The thirty young men swaggered up to him.

"We guessed it," they laughed. "What is stronger than a lion? What is sweeter than honey? We won—and you lost the bet."

Samson stared at them. Slowly he spoke. "If my wife had not told you, you would not have found out."

Slowly he stood. With one quiet move he kicked over the table. He strode from the room, and off down the road he went to the town of Ascalon, a proud stronghold of the Philistines. There he killed the first thirty men he saw, and stripped them, and took the thirty suits of clothes back to the bride's house to pay his bet.

No one dared stand in his way. No one moved. No one said a word. And Samson turned on his heel and went home to his father's farm. He was very angry, but as the weeks passed his anger cooled, and he began to feel he should forgive his wife. When the wheat harvest stood golden in the fields, Samson went back to Thamnatha, bringing a fine young goat as a present for his wife.

Her father met him at the door.

"She is not now your wife, Samson. I thought you hated her. I thought you had left her. She married the best man instead."

Samson's voice echoed like thunder through the town.

"From this day on I cannot be blamed for anything I do to the Philistines. And I will do you much evil!"

Samson left that house and went out into the woods. He called his Israelite friends to help him. Together they caught three hundred foxes. They joined those foxes' tails, two by two, tying them together, and to each knot they fixed a blazing torch. Then they drove the foxes into the Philistines' fields.

The wheat caught fire, the harvest was ruined. The vineyards were blackened and charred. Olive groves stood like forests of embers. The Philistines' crops were gone.

"Who did this?" cried the Philistines.

"Samson, because his wife was taken and given to another."

The Philistines were so angry and so afraid of Samson that they went and set fire to the bride's house and burned her and her whole family to death. They hoped to please Samson, but he was so outraged by their cruelty that he killed dozens of them in his wrath.

Then, when the Philistines lay quivering under his shadow, Samson left, and went alone into a mountain cave.

Now the land of the Philistines was large, and their armies were strong. Samson had made only the slightest dent in their armies with all his slaughter at Thamnatha. And when the rest of the mighty Philistines heard about it, they marched across the borders into Israel.

"We will put you all to death," they said, "unless you give us Samson as a prisoner, bound and tied."

The people loved Samson and honored him, but they loved their lives more. They went to the cave where the buzzards nested, and called up to Samson.

"Have you forgotten that the Philistines are our rulers? We cannot defy them. They will kill us all. We must tie you up, and give you to them as a prisoner."

Samson smiled. "Will you yourselves promise not to kill me on the way?"

"No. We will not hurt you. We will only tie you up!"

Samson came down and let them tie his arms with two new thick ropes, and as many knots as they pleased. He let them lead him to the city of Lehi, where the Philistine armies waited for him.

Shouts and catcalls and hoots dashed around Samson's

head. The Philistines circled around him waving their spears, and screaming for his death.

Samson stood still. He took a deep breath. The roots of his black hair tingled, and he felt the strength God gave him course through his veins. One stretch of his muscles, one swelling of his biceps and the ropes that bound him snapped like thread.

Spellbound, the Philistines watched as Samson stood free. So amazed were they that they did not move when he bent and picked from the ground an old sun-whitened jawbone of an ass. Who could have guessed, only five minutes before, that a thousand Philistines could be killed by one man swinging a donkey's jawbone?

That is exactly what Samson did.

"With the jawbone of an ass I have destroyed them," exulted Samson, singing out to the skies above. "With the jawbone of an ass I have killed a thousand men!"

Then he swung the jawbone around his head and flung it to the ground in the dust of the remaining Philistines who were running away. So afraid were the Philistines that their generals refused ever to go to war against Israel as long as the giant fought for them!

For twenty years Samson served as a Judge in Israel, and there was peace. The people were happy, but, sadly, Samson was not. He did not like peace. He was not thinking about the Lord, or about the people. He was thinking of himself. He wished he could be another Joshua, another Gideon. He knew he was not as great as they, and that made him sad. He longed for another chance to show how strong he was. He was bored.

Then Samson met a woman called Delilah. She was beautiful, gorgeous as a poisonous flower, and with one look she made him her slave.

The Philistines, who had kept constant watch on Samson, went secretly to Delilah.

"We've come to make a bargain," they said. "We want to know what makes Samson so strong. There have been others as tall, as broad, as thick—but never another so strong. Find out for us the secret of his strength, and tell us so we can overcome him—and we will give you, each one of us, eleven hundred pieces of silver."

Delilah walked to her window, the golden bells on her toes and ankles tinkling as perfume waved in the breeze.

I would be rich! she thought. And she said, "I will do it."

It was not easy. Samson still remembered the Philistine bride who pestered him for the riddle. Delilah would say:

"Tell me, Samson. I who love you want to know. What is the secret of your strength? What would someone have to do to tie you up and make you helpless?"

Samson answered her with nonsense. He told her that if he were tied with seven fresh bowstrings, he could not move. Then he told her that if he were tied with absolutely new ropes, he would be helpless. Then he told her that if she wound his seven locks of hair into a web and fastened them with a pin, he would be weak as a baby.

Each time Delilah would try what he said, and always Samson was as strong as ever. It became a sort of game between them. But finally Delilah grew angry and tired. She curled her arms around Samson's neck, and put her face close to his, and wept prettily.

"How can you say you love me when you keep secrets from me?" she whispered, stroking his iron muscles. "You have lied to me three times. You will not tell me the secret of your strength!"

Delilah would not leave him alone. She asked and begged

and pouted and complained and cried till Samson was tired of the whole business. At last he told her the truth:

"I am a Nazerite, dedicated to God from the day I was born. A razor has never touched my hair. If my head were shaved, my strength would be gone."

Delilah knew from his eyes that this time he told the truth. She went to the Philistines, and demanded her money, and told them Samson's secret. Together they schemed what she should do.

That evening she dressed herself as if for a feast, in purple and cloth of gold, with jewels on her ears and fingers and wrists and toes. When Samson came she greeted him like a king. She sang his favorite songs, and served the special fruit juices he loved. The air of the room was drowsy with perfume. The music was like a lullaby.

Samson grew sleepy, just as Delilah had planned. "Put your head on my lap," she whispered, "and forget the world and its cares."

Soon he slept. Delilah signaled. In a moment a little man hopped into the room, his razor gleaming in the lamplight. With the lightest touch the dwarfed barber snipped the seven locks of Samson's hair. Only five minutes, and never a flutter of the giant's eyelids, and his scalp was bare as a baby's.

The barber vanished. Delilah slapped Samson's face.

"Wake up—the Philistines are here, Samson!" she cried in a voice harsh as a crow.

Samson felt a chill on his head. He touched his skull, and knew what had happened. A dozen Philistines crowded over him with hot branding irons and put out his eyes. He screamed with pain.

Blind, helpless, a weakling, they led him off to the city of Gaza. The crowds screamed with glee at the sight of him. They took the once-mighty Samson and harnessed him like a donkey, and put him to work pulling a mill wheel, grinding wheat. Around and around he walked day after day, and if he faltered a whip cracked on his back.

The Philistines planned a great festival to their idol, a false god called Dagon. It would be a thanksgiving feast, a national holiday to celebrate the downfall of Samson. They spent weeks preparing. Thousands gathered for the celebration in the huge green granite temple. There was feasting and drinking and dancing and wild singing.

Then a cry went up, and the people demanded that Samson be brought out into the temple like a wild beast or a clown for them to jeer at. Blind and ragged, he was dragged from his prison and placed between the two main pillars of the temple for all to see.

"Look at the mighty muscles that grind wheat!" the people laughed. "Who was ever afraid of him?"

Samson stood listening. Much had happened to him in the weeks in prison. In his misery and his suffering Samson had learned more about God than he had known in all those years as a Judge. He had understood at last that it was only the Lord Who gave him strength. He had understood how weak he had been himself, and why the Lord had deserted him when he spent his strength and his time with the perfumed Delilah instead of in the Lord's service. Samson had been strong in body before. Now he was strong in soul.

He said to his guard, "Let me lean on these pillars and rest. I cannot see them. Put my hands out to touch them."

"Look!" cried the people. "The powerful Samson is so weak he must lean on a pillar!"

Samson was not fainting. He was praying. He knew that his hair had grown some during his weeks in prison. He knew too that his soul had grown.

"O Lord God," he breathed, "remember me, and restore

my strength. O my God, let me do justice for myself and for your people Israel!"

He put one hand on one pillar and one on the other. Through his body coursed the old thrill of power.

"Let me die with the Philistines!" he cried.

And, as the world has ever since remembered, he gave one great push with both his arms, and cracked the pillars, and ripped the temple apart. The temple collapsed, the stones fell on the Philistines and crushed every one of the thousands who had laughed and bowed before the false god.

In his death Samson had killed more than he had killed before in his life. Only in his death did he set the people of Israel free.

The Boy
Who Fought
a Giant

The Lord called His prophet Samuel.

"Fill your horn with holy oil, and go to Bethlehem. I have chosen a new king, whom you shall anoint."

Samuel now was old. His hair, his beard, even his eyebrows were white, but his heart was young and ready to obey. One question first, Lord, only one:

"Saul is still king. If he hears of it he will kill me. What shall I do?"

"You shall take a calf and say that you go to sacrifice. You shall summon the man called Jesse to the sacrifice."

Samuel did as he was told. He went to the little town of Bethlehem, where once the Moab girl Ruth had worked in the wheat fields and had fallen in love with Boaz. He called to him Ruth's grandson, Jesse.

When they were alone, Samuel asked Jesse to parade his sons, one by one, before him. Why? Any father would want to know. The old man would not tell, but something in his rock-strong eyes made Jesse obey.

As his stalwart sons marched past, Samuel prayed silently, and his heart listened for the Voice of the Lord.

First came Eliab, tall, handsome as any king.

"He must be the one," thought Samuel.

But the Lord said, "Look not on his face, nor his height. You see only the outward appearance, but the Lord looks on the heart."

One by one seven of Jesse's sons passed before Samuel, each strong and manly, with eyes of spirit and courage.

"The Lord has chosen none of these," said Samuel with a sigh. "Have you no more?"

Jesse smiled. "One more, but he cannot be the one you want. He is a shepherd. He's the youngest, and not like these at all. He makes up songs and poems, and plays music on a harp. Surely you would not want him."

"Bring him," said Samuel patiently.

From the hillside they brought Jesse's youngest son, the green stain of grasses on his bare feet. He was only a boy, dreamy-eyed, but something in his carriage spoke of strength and wisdom.

Samuel smiled at the boy, and the boy's cheeks dimpled with a valiant grin. His curly hair shone like copper. The Voice spoke in Samuel's ear.

"Arise, anoint him. This is he."

Samuel beckoned the youth still closer. "Your name?"

"My name," the boy replied, "is David."

Without another word Samuel drew out his vial and uncorked it, and poured the oil on the head of the shepherd boy. The spirit of the Lord came upon David.

Samuel and David had much to talk about in the days before the old Judge must return home.

Samuel sat with the boy on the grassy hillocks, watching

the sheep, and listened as he sang the songs which seemed to be seized from the skies. At first the old man had been afraid that this young dreamer could never be a true king. But as he listened he knew that in that slender body stood the spirit of a prophet, and a poet, and a warrior as well.

"You must wait here with your sheep," said Samuel. "The Lord will show you what you are to do, and when. Watch and pray, and wait as Abraham did, tending his flocks in Midian so long ago. Tell no one what I have done. Tell no one you are to be king."

David obeyed Samuel. He told no one. But the very fact that he had been secretly consecrated so excited him he could think of almost nothing else. He thought of the patriarchs and heroes of Israel—Abraham, Isaac, Jacob, Joseph, Moses, and Joshua. And, alone with his sheep, he sang songs of praise. Psalms, they were called then, and still are.

Among the white rocks and green fields of Bethlehem, David watched the seasons come and go, filled with wonder at the ways of birds and animals, and the sun and the moon and stars. The psalms he sang are with us today, in the book of the Bible. But in those days he lay in the hilltops of Bethlehem, almost unnoticed and unknown.

Then one day messengers came plodding across the sheep pasture with startling words. King Saul had sent for David!

Poor Saul! In his pride he had sinned against the Lord, and the spirit of the Lord had left him, and he was unhappy, not knowing why. He sat day after day buried in black gloom, doing nothing.

"This is an evil spirit troubling you," said his courtiers. "Let us find a skillful musician to cheer you!"

"Find me such a man," said Saul.

"There is one lad in Bethlehem—David. They say the Lord is with him, and he is a fine singer."

"Send David here!"

David came through the embroidered curtains of the throne room, a king in secret, before a king the Lord had doomed.

At first sight of him Saul was pleased. When David plucked the strings of his lyre and sang, a black spell of sadness seemed to vanish from Saul's heart. Saul loved him! He must have David near him, part of his court. And because the boy looked sturdy and fearless, Saul made him his armor-bearer, an unusual honor for one so young.

When the black moods came on Saul, David would sit quietly at the king's feet and sing. His hands made magic with the simple harp strings, and his voice rose clear and cool and gentle as he sang of the glory of the Lord.

Some courtiers whispered behind their hands:

"This is only a shepherd boy. Why should he be the king's favorite? Why should he have the honor of carrying Saul's spear and shield and armor? He can hardly stand up under the weight!"

David heard them, but he said nothing because though he was young he was also wise. He pretended to know nothing, but in his heart he promised himself someday to prove his worth to all who laughed at him now.

He did not have long to wait.

A giant was in the land. In the camp of the Philistines, ancient enemy of Israel, was a man ten feet tall, a huge champion named Goliath.

Goliath wore brass armor and a coat of mail which weighed more than two hundred pounds. The iron head of his spear weighed thirty pounds, and the staff of his spear was as thick as a weaver's beam. A strong man would stagger just lifting Goliath's spear. His shield was the largest ever seen, and his sword a fearsome blade.

Goliath strode at the head of the great Philistine army, his giant feet shaking the ground.

The Israelites under King Saul went out to meet them, shaking in their sandals. But this was to be no ordinary war. Goliath stood on the mountaintop and roared:

"Choose a man to meet me! If he kills me, we will be your servants. But if I kill him, then Israel shall serve the Philistines forever!"

Even Saul, brave as any king, was afraid. Who dared risk not only his own life but the freedom and glory of Israel in singlehanded combat with Goliath?

Day after day in the first light of dawning Goliath shouted his challenge. And when Goliath strode forward, the men of Israel turned and ran.

On the fortieth day young David came to camp, carrying some cheese and bread for his elder brothers who were soldiers. David himself had been sent home at the first sign of battle, an indignity he felt keenly. He clutched the food tightly and ran through the camp, looking for his brothers, when suddenly he heard the challenge of Goliath echo like thunder across the valley.

A soldier nudged David in the ribs. "Do you see that giant? To the man who kills him King Saul will give great riches, and will give him his daughter, the princess, to marry."

David listened, his eyes narrowing, his strong young chin hardening. Soon he stood before King Saul himself, and in his once-dreamy face shone a dauntless light.

"Let no one be afraid," said David. "I will go and fight with this Philistine!"

Saul's eyes flashed with admiration for such courage, but

he shook his head. "You are too young—and he has been trained as a warrior since he was your age."

David grinned. "I kept my father's sheep, you know. And often lions and bears took a ram from the flock. I would chase them, and snatch the ram from their mouths—and they would turn on me, and I strangled them and killed them."

With a leap David came closer to Saul. "I shall kill this Philistine as I did those beasts. Who is he that he dares curse the army of the living God? The Lord, Who delivered me from the lion's paw and the bear, will deliver me from the hand of Goliath."

Saul stood and said to David, "Go—and the Lord be with you."

Around him the men who had not had the courage to go themselves whispered:

"Why would he let this stripling go? Does he do it to shame us?"

"Perhaps the king is already tired of this little psalm singer, and wants to get rid of him this way!"

Saul led David to the place where his own armor was kept, which the singing David had carried and polished at court. Saul had thought him too young to carry the armor for him into battle. Now David should wear it, instead!

Saul himself put the royal helmet on David's head. Saul buckled the royal coat of mail, and handed him the royal sword.

David tried to whisper his thanks, but he could hardly

speak. The armor was too heavy, too big. He tried to walk and he staggered and fell with a clatter and a clash and a clang. The courtiers and officers burst into guffaws as the boy floundered helpless on the ground.

"I cannot go like this," said David to the king, and took off the armor.

David took his plain shepherd's staff, which he carried always. He went to a little brook near Saul's tent, and chose five perfectly smooth stones. And finally he took his sling, a pocketed thong of leather made to be whirled around the head, a homemade weapon he had often used to pitch stones at wolves and foxes. That was all.

"Go—and the Lord be with you!"

Goliath the giant came swaggering across the open field, his armor ringing and gleaming, and blinked his eyes in amazement. Across the tall grass a boy was strolling, a shepherd with a stick and a sling. The giant grinned and roared.

"Am I a dog that you come after me with a staff? I'll give your flesh to the birds of the air and the beasts of the field—in dainty bits!"

And David called back:

"You come at me with your sword and spear and shield. But I come to you in the name of the Lord, the God of the armies of Israel, Whom you have defied! This day will the Lord deliver you to me. I shall kill you and cut off your head—that everyone may know that the Lord saves, not with sword and spear, but by His might!"

Goliath's answer was a monstrous roar. But David did not flinch. Goliath lumbered forward, ready to cut the crazy, impudent upstart in half with one swoop of his sword. David did not step back. He hurried forward to the fight.

Swiftly he estimated distance and wind. From his shoulder bag he seized one of the five brook stones, put it in his slingshot, took aim, and whirled it round his head. Straight as an arrow the stone struck.

Like an ox smitten with an ax, Goliath crumpled to the ground. The stone had buried itself deep in his forehead.

David ran forward, losing not a moment. He seized the giant's sword and hacked off Goliath's head. Panting, he held aloft the dripping face against the brightening sky.

The Philistines fled in terror. And the soldiers of Israel, who had watched in fear for the moment of David's defeat, now rose in fiery strength and pursued the Philistines, killing many.

Abner, captain of the army, led the shepherd boy to the king. Down a maze of corridors they hurried, while David, exhausted and ragged, still carried the head of the giant, the blood spotting the palace floors.

Saul received David for what he was now, the hero of Israel.

Nearby stood Jonathan, Saul's own son, valiant warrior himself. And as Jonathan watched David, and listened to him, he knew he had found the dearest friend of his life, the one he could love more than any brother. He rushed forward to embrace him. David's robe was battle-stained. Jonathan gave him his own, and his sword, and his bow.

"What shall his reward be, Father?" cried Jonathan.

"He shall have riches. His family shall be honored, and freed from all taxes. And he shall be general of all the armies of Israel!"

David's cheeks flushed with pleasure, and he thanked the king.

But in his heart he thanked the Lord, Who had chosen him, and blessed him, and Who alone gave him the victory.

The Story
of David
and Saul

The smell of danger was in the palace. In the throne room
of old King Saul, whispers of peril met David's ears. The
shadow of hatred lowered silently over him in the gardens,
in the drill grounds, even in his bed.

Saul had been chosen by God, anointed by mighty Samuel
the prophet as king of Israel. But Saul had sinned and God
had rejected him as king. Samuel had told Saul that. Saul
knew that he must die, and that already the Lord had chosen
a new king.

David was that new king. David, the shepherd boy who
sang sweet psalms and fought mighty battles and slew
Goliath. David knew his destiny. Samuel had come to him
in Bethlehem, and blessed him, and told him what the Lord
commanded.

Saul did not know David's secret, but he hated David all
the same. Once he had loved him, rejoiced to hear him sing.
When David conquered Goliath, King Saul had rewarded
him, and made him general of all his armies.

Soon most of Israel took David to its heart. Jonathan, the

king's favorite son, was his best friend. Once when King Saul and David were returning from a victorious battle, the women of the cities came out to greet them with songs and dances. But their smiles and waving hands were not for King Saul. They were all for the ruddy-faced, curly-headed David, and over and over they sang a refrain:

> "Saul has slain his thousands,
> And David his ten thousands!"

Who could blame Saul for being angry? Already men whispered that David should be king. Jealousy boiled in Saul's heart. All night he sulked. By morning he was in a villainous mood.

"Send David here, to play the harp and sing!"

David had sung for Saul when he was a boy. Now he was a man, a general, but he came, obedient and gentle, trying to cheer the king with his music. Saul was determined to be difficult. Frowning and muttering, he sat on his throne, glaring, and finding fault. If he could make David burst out in anger, he would have an excuse to punish him.

"The harp is out of tune!" snarled Saul. "You're playing the wrong chords!"

David held his tongue. He would not be angry, and that maddened Saul beyond endurance. Saul suddenly sprang to his feet, seized his spear, and hurled it at David, trying to pin him to the wall. Only by inches did the huge javelin miss its mark. David ran from the throne room.

The boy general from Bethlehem told no one what had happened. But Saul was angrier than before. The fact that the spear missed bothered him. David seemed to lead a charmed life, protected by Heaven. *He must be destroyed!* thought Saul. *He is a general—let him be killed in battle.*

Saul sent David away from court, into active army service. He sent him on military adventures where any less lucky man, or one less blessed, would certainly have perished. But always David returned victorious, and more and more people cheered him and acclaimed his name.

How could Saul get rid of such a rival? In his hate-clouded mind he turned to his son, Prince Jonathan.

"Jonathan, my son, this David must be killed!" said Saul. "I know you love him and call him your friend, but listen! I am afraid he will make himself king—and you, my son, should be king after me. For your sake, David must die!"

Jonathan's face grew pale with horror. "Father—David has done nothing wrong! He fought the Philistines! He has served the Lord, and saved Israel. You saw it, and were proud of him. Why would you kill him?"

Father and son looked long at each other, and both remembered the day of battle when Saul had ordered Jonathan to die because he ate a mouthful of honey. The people saved Jonathan then. He saved David now from the murderous wrath of Saul.

"He shall not die," muttered Saul.

Meanwhile David hid himself at Ramah, near the home of Samuel, for he knew that secretly Saul still wanted to kill him. There, in a field at midnight, Jonathan came to him.

"What have I done?" cried David. "Why should your father seek my life?"

"You will not die," said Jonathan. "My father has promised me."

"He knows you are my friend," whispered David, "so he will hide it from you!"

"Tell me what to do, and I will do it," Jonathan declared, "for I love you more than if you were my own brother."

"Tomorrow is the new moon," said David, "and I should sit at the feast with the king, but I am going to hide in the fields for the three days of the feast. And when the king asks where I am, say that I have gone home to Bethlehem."

At the feast Saul noticed David's empty chair at once, but the king bided his time. On the first day he said nothing. On the second he scowled and demanded:

"Why does David not come to the feast?"

Jonathan explained: "He asked my permission to go to Bethlehem, to offer the sacrifice with his family."

"Asked permission? Of whom? Of you! Are you the king or am I?" roared Saul. "Bring David here, for he must die!"

Trembling and pale, but steadfast for his friend, Jonathan defied his father. "Why shall he be killed? What has he done to deserve it?"

Saul rose, and, taking his spear, he hurled it at his own flesh and blood. Once again he missed. He stood there cursing, calling down evil on Jonathan as the young man ran from the dining hall. But he did not dare ask his men to hold Jonathan, for everyone present, all the court, the bearded elders and generals at the feast, knew Jonathan had not deserved such treatment.

Stealthily Jonahan hurried to David.

"You must go and hide, as far away as possible. The king will hunt you down with soldiers and kill you!"

In the fields they made a pact of friendship, Jonathan and David, and promised to be loyal and true forever. Then the prince said:

"Go in peace. And let all stand that we have sworn. The Lord be between you and me forever."

Jonathan went back to the city.

And David, cut off from everything he loved, from his friends and his family, a runaway, an outlaw, doomed to death, made his way alone on dark roads.

Only one thing he had left, his faith and love for God.

More than any man since Adam, David understood the marvelous fact that God was not only his Lord, and his King, but his Father as well.

In the darkness he made a new psalm, in words dear to men for all time:

"You shall not be afraid for the terror by night, nor for the arrow that flies by day,

"Nor for the pestilence that walks in darkness, or the destruction that walks in noonday.

"A thousand shall fall at your side, ten thousand at your right hand, but it shall not come near you . . .

"Because you have made your home with the Lord, no evil shall befall you, nor affliction come near you.

"He will give His angels charge over you, to keep you in all your ways."

On the byroads, in the trails of beasts David wandered, fleeing for his life. But always with him was the knowledge that God the almighty Father was near him, hovering over him, waiting and hoping for his love. His soul was filled up with song:

"You know my downsitting, and my uprising. You know my smallest thought . . .

"There is not a word on my tongue, but You know it. You are behind me, and before me, and Your hand rests on me. . . .

"Where could I go from You? Where could I flee from Your presence?

"If I ascend to heaven, You are there. If I make my bed in the grave, behold, You are there.

"If I take the wings of morning, or dwell in the uttermost parts of the sea, even there shall Your hand lead me, and Your right hand hold me . . .

"The darkness hides me not from You, but the night shines as the day. Darkness and light are both alike to You . . .

"Search me, O God, and know my heart. Try me, and know my thoughts—and lead me in the way everlasting."

The hand of God was on his shoulder, as David walked in the way of danger.

"I will find him and kill him!" thundered Saul. "Though he go down under the earth to hide, I will find him."

David had nothing with him, no money, no food, no armor. Hunger gnawed at him as he ran through the deserts and hills. He came at last to a holy place, where the good priest Achimelech served the Lord.

"Have you any food?" cried David.

"I have no common bread," said the priest, "but only holy bread taken from the altar, so that new ones may be put there. If there is no sin in you, but only holiness, you may have that bread."

David ate, and then he asked, "Have you any weapons at all? A spear? Or a sword? I have none."

Achimelech knew David. A broad grin stretched over his holy face. "I have a sword for you—a sword like no other!"

He led David to the temple, and took out a blade wrapped in cloth. "Goliath's sword, David—the one you won. Take it!"

On David ran. Narrowly he escaped capture by the enemy Philistines, and by Saul, till he came to the Cave of Adullam, a great secret hollow in the hills not far from Bethlehem. There he settled down.

And soon, one by one, David drew to his side an army of merry men. His brothers, his cousins came, and men from all over who were discontented with the wickedness of Saul. Before long four hundred volunteers came to David's cave.

These were years of a precarious freebooter life for David and his men. They had brought their families to the wilds, and food must be plundered for them at the risk of capture. Free and wild their days were under the open sky, but always there was danger. Saul's soldiers hunted them like wolves. Always David and his followers must be on the jump, darting

and dodging from place to place. And though he must steal
to live, he never took food from the men of Israel, who were
his own people. Someday he would need them. He kept them
his friends.

Saul's fury grew day by day. When he heard that Achimelech had fed David and given him the giant's sword, he had
the whole company of priests there slain in cold blood.

But David's following increased with Saul's anger, reach-
ing six hundred, well hidden in the wildernesses. Saul could
not find David, but Jonathan, who loved him, did.

"David!" he called through the thickets. "David—fear not!
My father will never find you."

Together the two friends sat hidden in the branches of an
oak tree, pledging their friendship again.

"I know now," said Jonathan, "that you will be king." He
picked a leaf, studying its veins, and said softly, "I might have
been king after my father, but you will be instead. And I am
glad, for you are noble and strong as a king should be."

Soon, after Jonathan had left, David had a chance to show
the world exactly how fine a man he was.

David and his men were hidden in a cave, while all around
soldiers searched for them. Lost in the shadowy recesses, unseen, they saw King Saul, alone, unguarded, enter the cave
to rest a little in the coolness.

"Look!" whispered the men nearby silently. "Here is the day
the Lord promised you—when your enemy would be at your
mercy!"

So close was Saul that David sneaked up and cut a piece
off the hem of the royal robe.

"Now let us kill him!" whispered his men.

"No!" David's answer was firm. "The Lord forbid! I will
not! He is the Lord's anointed. He is the king, and he is my

master as well as my enemy. The Lord will do what is needed."

His men gasped. Could their leader be going soft? This is a crazy notion, they thought, to spare an enemy who thirsts for your blood! But they dared not disobey their leader.

Saul walked out of the cave unharmed. When he was far enough away, David called out:

"My lord the king!" And in the mouth of the cave he bowed. "Today I saved your life—see, here is the hem of your robe which I cut off! Why, then, do you seek to kill me?"

"David?" the king sobbed. "Is that your voice, David?" He whirled to face the cave, a beautiful amazement on his face. "You are far better a man than I! You have done good to me, and I have rewarded you with evil. This day the Lord put me at your mercy, and you did not kill me!"

Saul's fingers clutched at his torn red robe. "Who shows kindness to an enemy?" he whispered. "The Lord will reward you, David. And now I know that you shall surely be king!"

Saul stretched out his arms to David.

"Swear to me you will not kill my sons—you will not cut off my family's life?"

David swore. But he did not go to Saul. He knew perfectly well that, no matter what they agreed, Saul would soon change his mind and let his anger rise again.

David went back to his own men, and led them to safer places of hiding. And Saul went his way, the ragged hem of his robe trailing in the dust, constantly reminding him of the man who spared his life.

Soon after that the old and mighty prophet Samuel died. The whole country wept for him, and remembered how the Lord had called him as a boy, and given him victory over the Philistines, and used him to rule over Israel.

David, in the wilderness, wept too, but other problems pressed on him. His men were hungry. Nearby lived a rich man with a selfish, churlish temper, named Nabal. In the past David had protected Nabal's herds from desert raiders. Now he sent messengers to Nabal for food. And Nabal refused.

"Why should I feed some outlaws and tramps?" snorted Nabal. "Who is David that I should help him?"

But an hour or so later a strange caravan wound through the wild hills to David's camp, a woman with donkeys loaded with food. Abigail, Nabal's wife, brought two hundred loaves of bread, and five lambs ready to roast, corn and raisins and figs!

Tall and beautiful, Abigail stood before David, and her eyes saw the greatness that lay hidden in the future. She saw David, not as an outcast, but as a leader serving the Lord.

"Forgive my foolish husband," she said. "And—remember me!"

Abigail did not immediately tell Nabal what she had done. He was proud of having sent David away, and held a feast to celebrate. But ten days later the rich curmudgeon fell dead. When Abigail confessed her generous deed, he was so angry and so full of hate he dropped dead at her feet with a stroke.

And David asked Abigail to marry him. With a heart full of willingness, Abigail accepted, and came to the wilderness camp in her beauty.

Meanwhile, Saul raged again on the warpath against David. The memory of David's kindness had faded from his mind, as David had expected. Clouds of black hatred and fierce anger whirled around Saul's head. With three thousand men he marched against David.

From a high hill David watched them camp.

"A whole army against one man," he said. "They do me honor!"

"They haven't forgotten that you slew a giant single-handed," chuckled one of David's captains named Abisai.

"Who will go down with me to Saul's camp?"

"I will!" said Abisai.

Through the moonless dark they went, past the outposts of Saul's troops, past the sentries, stealthily to the edge of the royal tent.

Saul was asleep, his spear standing by his head.

Around him slept Captain Abner, who had been David's friend, and all the proud warriors of his army.

"One blow of the spear, and I will kill him!" whispered Abisai.

"Kill him not!" ordered David fiercely. "He is the Lord's! His day to die shall come."

Silently, without crackling a pebble under his feet, David knelt and took away Saul's spear and the cup of water at his side. No one waked as he and Abisai slipped from the camp.

From a far cliff David cupped his hands and roared:

"Abner! Answer me!"

Abner scrambled to his feet. "Who calls and disturbs the king?"

"Abner—you were guarding the king! Where is his spear? And his cup of water?"

Saul, his eyes staring madly into the darkness, groaned, "David again?"

"It is my voice, O King," laughed David. Torches from Saul's camp, flaring in the dark, gleamed on the spear and cup in David's hand.

"Come back, David! I will not harm you," croaked Saul.

"Send one of your young men to fetch the spear," called out David. "I shall not come to you. The mighty king of Israel has led his army out to catch a flea—and the flea will vanish! Farewell!"

Back in their forest caverns his men asked David:

"Why do you not kill Saul, and make an end of this running and hiding, this outcast life?"

Joab, his strongest captain, Abisai's brother, stood by the campfire. "David, tell us! Why does a man strong as you let his enemy live unpunished?"

The firelight glinted on David's copper hair, and painted strange shadows on his strong face.

"It is not for me to punish the man the Lord chose. Watch and see—Saul will destroy himself with his own sins!"

Months passed, with small wars, with danger and attacks and narrow escapes as David and his men watched and waited. Then word came that the Philistines, fiercest enemy of Israel, were massing new, vast, irresistible armies to destroy the kingdom.

Terror struck the evil soul of Saul. He prayed to the Lord, and the Lord did not answer. Desperately he clutched for help, and in his fear he committed a foul sin. He sought help from black magic, from a spirit medium, a woman called the Witch of Endor.

"Samuel helped me when he was alive," muttered the king. "I have no one now to help me!"

With prickling nerves and creeping blood Saul rode in disguise through the darkness across the valleys to a secret cave, where the wicked hag was hidden.

"Ghouls haunt these caves," whispered the soldiers behind Saul. "It is evil to go near the place!"

Skins of wild animals curtained the doorway.

"They say you can bring back the dead. Bring me back the one I want to see," said Saul in a low voice.

The Witch of Endor cleared her throat in the dank, cold cave and croaked: "Name the spirit!"

"Samuel!" Saul's voice shook. "Bring Samuel to me."

Her haggard eyelids drooped in the fiery glow. Gnarled brown hands came together behind her back. The shriveled body swayed as she muttered horrid, indistinguishable words. When at last she was silent, the stillness seemed never to end.

Saul shivered as he peered into the murky corners of the cave. What was to happen? Would he see the old prophet here in this place with this infernal woman and the dying fire in the chill restless air?

A gasp shook Saul. Something moved!

In the shadows beyond the hag a vapor coiled and shimmered, and grew, till it took the shape of a man, an old man with a white beard, a gleaming bald head, and luminous dark eyes—this was the ghost of Samuel.

Not by the words of a witch had Samuel come, but by the command of God, fitting punishment for Saul's sin.

The voice of Samuel echoed in the cave. "Why do you call me, Saul?"

"The Philistines are warring against me. Tell me what to do!"

"Why do you ask me? The Lord has turned from you. He will tear the kingdom from your hand and give it to David; because you did not obey the Lord. The Philistines shall triumph. And tomorrow you and your sons will be in the land of the dead!"

Before another sunset those words came true. Battle raged on the mountains. Saul fought bravely, without hiding, clear target for Philistine arrows. The arrows wounded him, but he remained alive to see three of his sons slain by the enemy. And one of his dead sons was Jonathan.

Then Saul's heart broke, and he did not wish to live in defeat. He called his armor-bearer.

"Draw your sword, and kill me," commanded the king.

But the armor-bearer was afraid, and quailed until Saul, roaring curses, seized the sword himself and fell upon it. The next day the Philistines found the dead king, and cut off his head, and hung his body from their city wall, and put his armor in the temple of the heathen god.

And David, hearing of it, lamented and wept. He was king now, but his eyes were filled with tears for Saul, who had been king, and who had failed to walk with the Lord.

The Wisest
Man
in the World

A young king climbed to the high hill of Gabaon to worship the Lord.

His name was Solomon, and he was a new king in Israel. His father, glorious King David, had died only a little while before.

The Ark of the Covenant, the sacred altar of God, stood on this hill. The court and all the great men of Israel walked with the king, in their scarlet robes and their ornaments, to watch him offer sacrifice to the Lord. A thousand perfect lambs Solomon offered. The smoke of holocaust rose to the sky. In pomp and majesty Solomon stood.

"He is like his father," men whispered, "so strong, so handsome, so proud! Here indeed is a king!"

When the sacrifices were done, the people went home. But Solomon stayed on the hill of Gabaon, to study his own heart.

"Any man can wear a crown," said Solomon to the evening winds, "but to be a good king is hard. A king must keep peace. He must govern, and judge, and plan, and build."

King David had conquered the enemies of Israel and built a mighty empire. Could his son hold it together? King David had kept the people close to the Lord. Could Solomon?

To himself Solomon whispered the truth. He was afraid of making mistakes, of endangering his people, of failing in this great task. Alone on Gabaon, he breathed a prayer, and, alone, he went to sleep.

In his dream a Voice spoke. A Voice called his name, the Voice of the Lord, Who had spoken to Abraham, and Isaac, and Jacob, the great Voice of the one true God:

"Solomon! Choose any gift, and I will give it to you! What would you have Me give you?"

Humbly Solomon answered: "To my father David, You showed great mercy, while he walked in the paths of Your righteousness. Now, O Lord, my God, You have made me king instead of my father. And I am only a child, Lord. I know so little!"

Solomon took a deep breath. "I ask You to give me an understanding heart. Make me wise so that I may judge Your people, and know the truth!"

The Voice of the Lord answered:

"Because you asked for wisdom, and not for a long life, or for riches, behold, I have done as you asked! I have given you a wise and understanding heart. There was never before one like you, and never will be."

Solomon bowed his head, but the Lord still spoke:

"I give you also the things you did not ask. You shall have greater riches and more honor than any other king. And if you walk in My ways, and keep My commandments as your father David did, then I will give you a long life."

Almost immediately King Solomon met with a test for his wisdom, a test to be remembered forever.

Two women stood before his throne, a red-haired one on the right, a dark-haired one on the left. Between them on the floor lay a straw basket, and in it a baby, playing with his toes.

"The child is mine," said the red-haired woman. "This woman's child died in the night, and she took my baby while I was sleeping, and now she says it's hers, and that my baby is the one who died."

The other shook her head fiercely. "It's a monstrous lie! The baby is mine! Hers died, and she's trying to take my baby away by saying I stole hers!"

The people of the court shook their heads and looked at Solomon. "Only the wisest of men could solve that problem," they whispered. "Solomon is a good king, but he is so young! What can he do? How could any man be certain whose child this was? No one was there to see!"

"Bring me a sword!" commanded Solomon.

The armor-bearer hurried to fetch it. The courtiers raised their eyebrows in alarm as he carried the long blade with the great golden guard and handle, and the golden chain jangling.

King Solomon looked from one woman to the other. He lifted the sword. The shimmering blade hung just over the baby's heart.

"Let the child be cut in two!" said the king. "Give half to one, and half to the other."

A scream echoed through the throne room. The dark-haired woman was crying: "No! No! Never! Give the child to her, but let it live! Do not kill it!"

In the same breath the red-haired woman was saying: "Let the child be neither yours nor mine. The king is right. Divide it!"

Solomon stroked his brief brown beard, dark eyes gleaming as he listened to both at once. He bent down and picked up the baby, and gave it to the arms of the dark-haired woman.

"It is your child, and you are his true mother," said Solomon. He wheeled in fury on the red-haired woman. "Only a woman wicked enough to steal a baby would agree to see a living child divided by a sword. A mother cannot bear to see her child killed. You gave yourself away!"

The men of the court grinned. "He is young—but have you ever seen a man so wise?"

The Lord had kept His promise to Solomon!

Young as he was, Solomon seemed to know everything about everything. He could talk about the plants that grow, and all the animals. He understood the ways of rich men and poor, of how to raise children, and how to deal with fools. He knew the laws of heaven and earth, the goodness of the Lord, and the weakness of men. The words of Solomon filled many books. Three thousand of his sayings called Proverbs are in the Bible, and poems of his, and parables, and studies about God.

War was dead under such a wise king. Everywhere in Israel a man could sit under his vine and his fig tree without worry or fear.

"Now," said King Solomon, "the time has come to build a Temple for the Lord!"

Up to the hill of Gabaon he climbed again, to pray before the altar of the Lord, and the tent which covered the sacred Ark of the Covenant. Solomon remembered all the glorious history of that tabernacle.

To Moses on Mount Sinai the Lord had given the Ten Commandments, written on stone. At the Lord's command Moses had built a home for those stone tablets, an Ark, a box of wood covered with gold and mounted with cherubim.

The Ark and the altars were placed in a tent as the Lord wished, to travel with His people to the Promised Land. Over that Ark the pillar of cloud had shone through forty years in the wilderness. The walls of Jericho had tumbled; the waters of the Jordan had parted. There was nothing holier in Israel than this, the sign of God's promise to man.

My father David dreamed of a Temple, and the Lord said his son should build it, thought Solomon. *What greater thing could I do?*

He told the people his plans. "The Temple shall be a marvel of beauty, to show all peoples the greatness of our God."

Solomon sent to King Hiram of Tyre, the king who had helped David build the palace of Jerusalem. In Hiram's land grew fine cedar forests. His people were traders of the seven seas, with stores of gold and ivory and precious stones. And these Solomon needed for the Temple.

A wall of stone and cedar would enclose a large courtyard, with room for burnt sacrifices, and for all the people to gather. The Temple itself would not be too large, about thirty feet by a hundred and four, but it would be a masterpiece of perfection. Inside would be the sanctuary, and, behind a violet and scarlet veil, the Holy of Holies, where the Ark would stand.

Blood-red cedar were the walls, the doors of solid olive wood, the floor of precious marble. And everywhere carvings of angels and palm trees and flowers were overlaid with deep-shining gold and jewels.

More than seven years men worked in quarries and in forests. When at last the final sheet of gold was laid on, the scaffolding was torn down, the tattered coverings torn away, and all Israel came to see the wonder.

From Gabaon's hill to Jerusalem priests carried the Ark of the Lord. Around them marched the choirs King David had trained, with cymbals and harps and lyres, and one hundred and twenty trumpeters, and singers, praising the Lord.

The Ark entered the Temple, entered the sanctuary, on the shoulders of the priests. And, before the eyes of everyone, an amazing thing happened.

The Temple was filled with a cloud. The glory of the Lord had filled this new house of God. Silvery fog swirled in the inner Temple, a fog so dense that the priests could not enter, but only fall to the ground in worship till it passed away.

Solomon stood before the people. "The Lord promised to dwell in a cloud, ever near the Ark. In a pillar of cloud and fire He traveled with our fathers. But I have built Him a house to His name that He might live there forever."

Then King Solomon knelt before all the people, and raised his hands to heaven.

"Lord God of Israel, can it be that God should live with man on earth? The heaven of heavens cannot contain You! How much less this house I have built!

"I built it only that here You might hear our prayer from Your firm dwelling place above. I built it so that from heaven You would hear us, and open Your eyes on this house day and night!"

Silence fell as Solomon finished. On the altars the lamb of sacrifice waited for the priests to kindle a fire and burn it for the Lord. In the silence, while all watched, and the priests stood still far away, flame leaped from heaven to the altar, tongues of fire consuming every trace of the sacrifice.

The glory of the Lord filled His Temple, so blinding, so magnificent, that not even the priests dared enter.

Seven days Israel feasted to music and praised the Lord. Never since the blessed days of Adam in the Garden of Eden had man been so certain of the presence of God!

Solomon slept in his royal bed, his heart soaring with pride for all that he had done for the Lord.

That night the Voice of the Lord called him:

"Solomon! I have heard your prayer, and blessed the Temple you have built. I shall hear the words of anyone who prays in this place.

"As for you, if you keep My words and My law, I shall make your sons and their sons kings in this land forever. But if you turn away from Me, and go to serve strange gods and adore them, I will pluck you out by your roots, and I will abandon the Temple to your enemies!"

After the Lord had gone, Solomon lay staring into the dark, the heavenly warning ringing in his ears. Turn to strange gods and idols? Ridiculous! Solomon knew the suffering that punished sin, in Eden, and a thousand times since.

"There is nothing new under the sun," Solomon had said so many times. In the years since the gates of Eden had closed God the Father had had His line of heroes, from Noah to Abraham, from Samuel to David. Now Solomon stood in that line, schooled by the whisper from heaven that heroes hear.

"I am too wise to sin," said Solomon. "I know what has happened in the past."

The Lord had promised Solomon riches and power, too. He had more than the world could believe. His income was about six hundred sixty-six gold talents a year, or about twenty million dollars. He had seven hundred wives, and for them he built a palace near the Temple.

"I think," said the men of the court, "that Solomon would do anything his wives asked!"

Tales of this king's wisdom and riches reached the far corners of the earth. Travelers, camel drivers, and boatmen told about him in every camp. And, from a kingdom far to the south, in Arabia, the magnificent Queen of Sheba heard of Solomon's glory and decided to come to see the truth for herself.

My land, Sheba, is rich in stones and rainbow gardens. We have incense, myrrh, spices, and gold. Nothing can be grander than this! thought the dark-skinned queen. *What is Israel? They were slaves in Egypt once, and wandered around in a desert, and spent most of their time quarreling —they're wild tribes!*

The Queen of Sheba came to Jerusalem decked in her finest. A diamond diadem gleamed on her forehead. Bangles of star sapphires hung from her wrists and ears. Her long caravan of camels nearly staggered under sacks of gold.

Solomon greeted her in his palace. His eyes laughed silently as she stared at his giant throne of beaten gold and carved ivory, its steps guarded by twelve stone lions. He nodded as she looked in wonder at the walls lined with three hundred huge golden shields.

"Israel is a house of treasure!" breathed the queen.

Many days she stayed talking with Solomon, testing his wisdom with problems. Always the peoples of the East had considered themselves the wisest in the world. Could a man of these tribes of Israel know as much?

"Never," said the Queen of Sheba, "was a man wiser or richer than this king of Israel! I shall tell the world that this people is a nation fit to stand anywhere."

The Chosen People of the Lord had come a long way from their days of slavery in Egypt. For this the Lord had blessed Solomon with riches and understanding, that the world could see and marvel at His power, the power of the God of Israel!

But, as Solomon bid the queen farewell, she smiled again

and said: "I believe you have made yourself the greatest king ever!"

And he did not try to contradict her. The trouble was, Solomon was beginning to believe just that. He was beginning to forget that all he had was a gift from the Lord. The wisest man in the world was about to play the fool!

Proudly Solomon went back to his palace, and into the jaws of trouble. His wives were angry, and their voices clamored and jarred the embroidered hangings.

Seven hundred wives—enough to make a whole town—are more than an ordinary man can handle. Solomon could have done it because he was no ordinary man, but he had made some serious mistakes. Some of his wives were good women of Israel, faithful to the Lord. But others Solomon had chosen from far-off lands. One of his wives was a daughter of Pharaoh, a princess from Egypt, where Israel had been captive till the days of Moses. The daughters of all his enemies Solomon had made his wives—Moabites, Edomites, Hittites, and Ammonites.

"If I marry their women they will not fight against me," Solomon had said. "There will be peace in the world."

But not at home! These women from other lands did not go to the Temple to pray to the Lord. They worshiped strange gods, in dark and evil ways. They prayed to the idol Baal, to Astarte, and to bloodthirsty Moloch. At first they had worshiped in secret. But now they said:

"Solomon! Build us temples, too, for our gods."

"I cannot," said King Solomon.

"But you are the king. And the wisest man on earth. The laws are not for people like you!"

Solomon nodded. "There is no king like me."

"You have your Lord God. But it is cruel to say that we cannot have our gods. You must be broad-minded!"

They begged him, pleaded with him, sang to him, smiled for him, shouted at him, screamed, and cried:

"Build us a temple, too!"

Solomon did.

Solomon, who had built the Temple to the one true God, went out and built two temples to false gods—one for the idol with gruesome eyes called Chamos, and one for the fiendish god of filth and murder called Moloch.

"I am the wisest man in the world!" said Solomon, his black eyes gleaming. "All gods are mine, and one is as good as another!"

And, having built the temples, Solomon went in them, and bowed before idols, and kissed their painted feet, burned incense to them, and called them gods.

That night Solomon walked alone, away from the sound of his wives, alone with his thoughts of his own greatness.

"Solomon!" The Voice of the Lord cut like a cold sword.

"You have broken My law, and turned your heart against Me. Because of this, I shall tear your kingdom to bits, and give it to one of your servants!

"But, for the sake of your father David, I will not do it while you still live, and I will not take the whole kingdom away. Your son shall have one tribe, for the sake of David and Jerusalem, which I have chosen."

In the dark night Solomon's dreams of glory crumpled around him. His empire, which he thought would be for all time, would fall to ruin. War would rise again. Destruction would plummet down on Israel.

Slowly Solomon spoke.

"Wisdom I asked for. Wisdom I received. But wisdom alone cannot save a man's soul. The keenest mind will not keep a man from sin. It will lead him to it, because it swells him with pride."

Pride! It was pride that made Adam and Eve sin. Pride lay coiled under every sin in history, in Moses, in Saul, in David, and in Solomon. When man thinks of himself before God, pride strikes the blow of death.

"Nothing new under the sun," Solomon murmured.

He stood and stared at the stars.

"The Lord promised punishment for Israel. He promised none for me. But I know why. He gave me wisdom. And for the rest of my life my own wisdom will punish me with an understanding of the awful thing I have done."

And he asked the Lord to save him. He knew he could not save himself.

Elijah
the Prophet

A man was marching down the road, a wild fellow in the rain, his hair wet and streaming down to the small of his sunburned back, his beard blowing around his knees in the wind.

The people in the kingdom of Israel saw him coming, and went out to see.

"He looks like a prophet," the old men said.

He went through the mud barefoot. His enormous, gnarled hands were clasped as if he prayed even while he ran. His enormous eyes were glistering with joy, as if he fully understood what he saw and heard as he watched the sky, never looking at the ground, although he had run many miles.

The people watching, wondered, and the old ones thought back across the years to the last time a prophet of the Lord had come.

So much had happened in those years since the people became two kingdoms, Israel and Judah. Prophets had been heard in the days of the first king of the new Israel, Jeroboam the wicked, who worshiped golden calves. But there had been none in Israel since.

Six kings had sat on the throne since then, following each other in blood and murder. King Nadab, Jeroboam's son, had been killed by Baasa. King Baasa's son, King Ela, was killed by the captain of his army, Zambri. And the fierce general Omri killed King Zambri, burned him to death in his palace. Omri had built a new palace, in the city of Samaria, and there his son Ahab now was king.

"All this time the Lord has been silent," the old men whispered, "while all around us idols stand, and no one dares worship the God of Israel openly."

"Queen Jezebel killed all the prophets! How could this be one?"

Almost silently an old man answered. "Not all! Obadiah, King Ahab's own steward, saved a hundred of them secretly in a cave, and fed them."

They watched the man running in his cloak of wild skins, and wondered.

"If he is a prophet of the Lord," they said, "he will meet the wickedest rulers of all—King Ahab and his evil queen, Jezebel."

On the man ran through the hot summer storm.

"Who are you?" the sentries of Samaria called.

"Elijah!" he said. "I have run a hundred miles and more, to see King Ahab."

They made him wait in the courtyard while they asked the courtiers of His Majesty. The people standing around circled him, staring at him, trying to guess what sort of fellow he was. They could not know that they were in the presence of one of the great men of history, this Elijah, who is also called Elias.

"There is fire in his eyes," they said. "Perhaps he comes to honor our gods."

Elijah listened, and held his tongue. He knew their gods. Anger leaped in his throat at the thought of the evil King Ahab had done, of the evil that stood at his side as queen, the woman called Jezebel. She, a Syrian, it was who really ruled Israel. She, beautiful as only the devil's daughters can be, had brought her own gods to Israel, Baal the idol, and Melkart and Asherah. Four hundred and fifty idol priests she had brought with her to rule in the temple of Baal, which Ahab built. The people who loved the Lord God of Israel, and said so, she killed.

The sentries returned and marched the stranger into the throne room. King Ahab, on his gilded chair, took one look, and then grinned at his redheaded Queen. Surely this fellow is mad!

But the tattered prophet gave the king no time to speak.

"As the Lord God of Israel lives," cried Elijah, fixing Jezebel with his fierce eyes, "as the Lord my God lives, no rain shall fall in this land for all these years, unless by my own word!"

Ahab snorted. "Is that all? The man is mad—not a prophet, but a crackpot!"

One of his courtiers, cocking his left ear, waved a warning finger.

The drumming sound on the roof top had suddenly stopped. The courtier ran to the window and pulled back the green and yellow draperies. The sun was shining. The rain had ended.

"Summer rains always end quickly," said Queen Jezebel. "Get the man out of here. I shall not even punish him for speaking of his Lord. You don't punish a man who is crazy!"

She waved her fan with perfumed fingers. Elijah was shoved out into the muddy road and told to go.

"Go to the east, to a cave near the brook of Carith," the Voice of the Lord sounded secretly in Elijah's ears. "You shall drink of the water torrents, and I have commanded the ravens to feed you there."

Elijah went, and for months no one thought any more about him. The king and queen forgot him at once. He lived in the cave by the rushing waters, and prayed, and grew in the spirit of holiness. Morning and night, big black birds circled over his barren crag, bringing grain and bread and berries and meat in their huge beaks.

And no longer, anywhere in Israel, did a drop of rain fall. No dew sparkled in the morning grass.

The brook of Carith grew smaller in the sun. Only a trickle was left when the Voice of the Lord said:

"Elijah! Go now to the town of Sarephta in Sidon. I have commanded a widow woman there to feed you."

The ravens blackened the sky in flight over the dry and cracked mud of the brook bed, croaking a harsh farewell. Elijah took his staff, wrapped his animal skins around him, and came out of the wilderness. Mile after mile he trudged northward, across Israel to the land of Sidon, where Queen Jezebel had been born. He did not know why the Lord sent him there to a land of idols. He did not ask; he obeyed.

At the gate of the city an old woman gathered firewood. The eyes of the prophet picked her out.

"May I have food, and water?" he said.

"Water you may have," she said. "But by the Lord your God I have no bread. I have only a handful of meal in a barrel, and a little oil in a bottle. I am gathering wood to cook that for me and my son, and when it is eaten we shall die of hunger."

Elijah smiled kindly through his fierce, wind-tossed beard. "Don't be afraid," he said. "Go make me a little pancake, and then fix some for you and your son."

He bent down from his tallness till he looked straight into her face.

"The Lord God of Israel has said that never will your barrel of meal be empty, and never shall the oil be gone from that bottle, until the day He sends rain on the earth."

His words came true. She fixed his pancake, and the meal for herself and her son, and the barrel of meal and the bottle of oil were full. Day after day, no matter how much they took out to use, the food containers were full.

The woman's eyes popped. She bubbled with thanks.

"Stay here, with us, forever, you man of wonders!" she said.

But not long after her son suddenly fell sick. In the space of an hour he was dead. In her grief the widow whirled on Elijah: "You have killed him! Some power you have, some black magic—why did you do this? My son is dead!"

"Give me your son," said Elijah. Grunting, he lifted the body of the boy in his arms, and carried him up to his own room. Alone with the dead, Elijah prayed, crying out to the Lord to give back the life taken so young. Closer and closer he hugged the young dead boy, as if he could warm him back to life. And over and over he prayed. . . .

When the widow heard Elijah calling her hours later, she scrambled up the stairs. In the doorway stood her son, alive. "Truly, you are a man of God!" sobbed the widow. "The word of the Lord in your mouth is true."

For three years there was meal in the barrel and oil in the bottle. Then in the third year of drought the Voice of the Lord said to Elijah:

"Go to King Ahab. And I will send rain on the earth."

When day followed day, weeks, months, and still no rain, King Ahab had remembered Elijah. The land was dry, nothing grew, and the fields were like ashes. Urgent messengers Ahab sent to find the hairy hermit, a long, heartbreaking search. For three years not a day had passed that Ahab's men had not looked for the stranger who told the king there would be no rain.

Famine's hands were at Israel's throat. Hunger clutched at the kingdom. On the horizon appeared the wild and shaggy figure of the prophet.

First to see him was the steward of the king, Obadiah, who long ago had hidden the prophets of Israel in caves and saved them. Swiftly he ran to Ahab, across dusty hills where now no grass grew.

"Elijah is come!"

The king hurried out on foot, purple robes flapping at his heels, down the dry roads after Obadiah, till at last he met Elijah.

"Are you the one who brought this trouble on Israel?" gasped the king.

"Not I, but you," answered Elijah.

"What have I done? I love my people. I did not stop the rain. You did!"

"You turned away from the Lord, and followed a false god—Baal!"

The king blinked in astonishment. "It's a small matter, which god you worship. One god's as good as another!"

"There is only one true God!" thundered Elijah. "Only one! You shall see!"

Then Elijah proposed a strange test, a public contest—a duel of prayer.

"Bring the prophets and priests of your idol Baal, all of them, including the four hundred who eat at Queen Jezebel's table. Bring those to Mount Carmel, all eight hundred and fifty of them. There we shall see which is the true God—your Baal, or the God of Abraham, of Isaac, of Jacob and Moses and Joshua, of David and Solomon!"

"A fair challenge," King Ahab agreed.

At his command all the prophets of Baal left the temple and the groves of their idols. At his word all the people of the kingdom left their homes and farms and businesses. Everyone went to the green-wooded mountain of Carmel, near the shining blue sea.

Elijah faced the crowds:

"You must choose! If the Lord be God, follow Him. But if Baal is, then serve him.

"I am the only prophet of the Lord here. Baal's prophets are in the hundreds. But alone I challenge them. Let them bring two bullocks, one for them, and one for me. Let them cut theirs to pieces, and lay it on wood on their altar, without lighting a fire. I will do the same on the altar of the Lord. Then let them call on the name of Baal, and I will call on the name of the Lord. The God that answers by fire—let him be God!"

The people answered the challenge with a scream of excited agreement.

The priests of Baal did not like this extraordinary contest, but they saw no way to escape it. "King Ahab will try anything to get rain," they muttered to each other, "even such a mad battle of prayer as this. For surely, who can make fire can make rain."

The two bullocks lay dead on the piles of firewood. Smilingly Elijah insisted that Baal's priests make the first try. Their leader began with a long speech, bragging about what they were going to do, and delaying as long as he could.

Then the priests of Baal began to pray. They did not believe Baal could send fire. In their hearts they knew it was impossible. But they tried.

They crept forward on their hands and knees, chanting heathen litanies, while their helpers whirled fragrant torches overhead and clashed brazen cymbals. A whole morning the followers of Baal prayed and chanted. But all in vain.

"Cry louder!" mocked Elijah. "Maybe your god is on a journey. Or maybe he is asleep, and must be awakened."

The priests of Baal milled around, cutting their own arms and legs with knives in their frenzy. Hour after hour they clapped their hands and chanted magical words in solemn and ever-faster rhythms. Still no answer from Baal.

Then, Elijah took twelve stones and built a special altar for his bullock, with a trench around it and under it.

"Throw water—sea water, twelve barrelfuls on the bullock. And fill the trench to overflowing!" commanded Elijah. And men poured water over it all till it was soaking, sopping, drenching wet.

One disdainful look Elijah threw on the priests of Baal. Pagans! Unbelievers! his eyes seemed to say. Then Elijah lifted up his hands and prayed:

"Lord God of Abraham, Isaac and Israel, let it be known this day that You are God in Israel, and that I am Your servant, and that I follow Your word. Hear me, O Lord, hear me, that this people may know You are the Lord God!"

The answer was instantaneous and terrifying. Whole sheets of fire fell from the skies. Flames leaped at the wood and the bullock, and devoured them, and the stones and the dust itself. Fiery red-orange tongues licked up every drop of the water.

"The Lord, He is the God!" roared the people, again and

again, and again, shaking fists at the dumfounded priests of
Baal.

"Take the prophets of Baal, and let not one of them escape," Elijah roared back. The false prophets died there.

Then Elijah spoke to King Ahab, who cowered on the
ground. "Get up! Eat, and drink, for there is the sound of
rain."

Without waiting for a reply the prophet went to a cave on
the top of Mount Carmel, and lowered his face between his
knees in prayer.

"Look to the sea," he called to his servant.

The man looked and saw nothing.

Seven times Elijah told him to look down on the Mediterranean, and on the seventh time he said: "I see a cloud rising
out of the sea, a little cloud no bigger than a man's foot."

"Then go to King Ahab," said Elijah. "Tell him to get into
his chariot and hurry down from the mountain before the
rain stops him!"

The small cloud grew, and twisted and swelled in the sky,
till it blackened and covered the land. The winds were blowing a gale. And the rain fell in torrents upon the thirsty
earth.

King Ahab rode through the storm, from the altar of God,
back to Jezebel, the wicked queen.

And Elijah stood in the storm on the mountaintop, praising
the Lord.

The Story
of
Jonah

The man named Jonah, who lived in the land later called Galilee, was a good man who served the Lord, and worshiped Him, and believed in Him.

He was one of the few people left in the land of Israel who did follow the Lord. The ugly faces of idols loomed in strange temples, and golden calves stood on altars that should have belonged to the Lord.

"It is hard to understand," said Jonah, "but the people seem determined to turn their hearts away from the Lord, no matter what miracles he works, or how great his prophets are."

That was true. The Lord had sent Elijah, and Elisha, two of the most amazing miracle-workers ever seen, to bring Israel away from the wickedness of idols. And Elisha had anointed a king, a man of Judah, named Jehu, who smashed the figures of Baal and killed all the idol priests in a bloody year of reform.

Yet King Jehu himself made golden calves, and worshiped

them, thought Jonah as he dug the weeds from his rows of corn. *And his son Jehoahaz was a weak king, and let Israel be nearly destroyed by the Syrians and their King Hazael. Only Elisha the prophet saved us then! On his deathbed he promised that Syria would be defeated, and it was.*

He leaned on his hoe, and raised his face to the sky. "Oh, Lord," he prayed. "Israel needs a new prophet. We are in danger again!"

A new power had risen in the world, the men of another land called Assyria, a little farther north. Anyone with a grain of sense knew that the time was coming when the Assyrian war chariots would fall on Israel and devour it like wolves slathering over a fallen deer.

"But the men of Israel are not thinking," sighed Jonah as he slashed at the thistles in his field. "They are too rich, and too fat to think—or pray!"

Israel had a new king, another Jeroboam, and under him the country had become extremely wealthy. Men built fine town and country houses, decked with silken upholsteries and ivory-inlaid divans. People were busy buying silks and brocades brought by caravans from the East, and jeweled headdresses, and rings, and bracelets, and necklaces of precious stones. The air was filled with the sounds of feasting and music. And the golden calves still stood on the altars. Men spoke piously of the Lord God of Israel, but they burned incense before the statues of the baby cows instead.

Jonah went on weeding, and praying, and thinking, when suddenly the wind seemed to stop, and even the noise of the bees, and a strange strong Voice filled the air. It was the Voice of the Lord, calling a new prophet—calling Jonah!

"Go, Jonah, to the great city of Nineveh, and preach there, for the wickedness of that city is great!"

Nineveh? The thought of such an undertaking terrified Jonah. He knew that Nineveh was the chief city of the terrible land of Assyria, a huge place of grandeur and magnificence. The walls around it were a hundred feet high, and broad enough on top for three chariots to race along side by side. The city was big, so huge that it would take a man three days to walk around it.

"Go to Nineveh and preach!"

To Nineveh? Jonah shook his head, and rubbed his eyes.

"The Lord cannot mean for me to go to Nineveh," he said to himself. "Everyone knows that the people of Israel are the chosen people of the Lord. What would His prophet be doing in Nineveh? The people there are heathens. The Lord doesn't care about them."

Jonah thought about it all that evening, as he ate his bread and cheese, as he lay down and tried to sleep. Finally he decided:

"I must have misunderstood that Voice. Or else it was not the Voice of the Lord. I will not go to Nineveh." And then, because he was not sure of his own thoughts, he decided it would be wiser to go somewhere else as quickly as he could.

In the seaport of Joppa he found a trading ship, bound for the farther end of the Mediterranean Sea. He paid his fare and went aboard.

Hardly was the ship out of the harbor when out of a clear sky a tremendous gale blew up. Waves dashed over the bow. The masts and sails faltered in the storm. The decks pitched from side to side.

"The ship will break apart!" the sailors cried. "We will wreck!"

"Throw overboard everything you can!" roared the captain. "Lighten the load. Throw over all the goods we are carrying to sell. Perhaps the presents will appease the gods of the sea!"

Bales of silk, carved chairs and bedsteads, whole sacks of gold they threw overboard, but the storm only grew in intensity, howling like some devil bent on destroying them. The sailors, who were from the pagan land of Phoenicia, called on all their gods to save them, and still the storm screamed and twisted the ship.

Jonah, the only paying passenger on the ship, was asleep below decks. The storm did not seem to bother him at all. Soon the captain was shaking his shoulder.

"Why are you asleep? Get up, and pray to your God, and ask Him to save us!"

And, while Jonah prayed, the seamen had an idea.

"This storm is like a punishment from heaven. Some god is trying to destroy us! Let us cast lots and see which one of us on this ship is causing this evil."

Waves dashed high over the slippery deck. Men clung to ropes and spars, as one by one they drew lots. Number after number came up, and finally the accusing one fell on Jonah.

"Tell us why this evil has come on us!" they screamed at him over the wind. "Who are you, and what is your business? Where do you come from?"

Jonah set his feet firmly on the water-swept deck. "I am a Hebrew," he said, "and I fear the God of heaven, Who made both the sea and the dry land."

"It is you who have brought the storm! What have you done to anger this God of yours?"

In the teeth of the gale Jonah confessed what he had done. "I disobeyed the Voice that sent me to Nineveh. I ran, the other way!"

"What shall we do with you, to make this storm end?"

Wretchedly Jonah cried, "Throw me into the sea!"

The seamen did not want to do it. They tried to turn the ship out of the storm, tried desperately to steer it to safe harbor. But it was too late in those raging seas. They could do nothing.

Finally, with a prayer that the Lord would not punish them for Jonah's death, the crew tossed the pale-faced passenger over the side.

As Jonah's body touched the water, the storm stopped. The tempest was stilled. As the body of Jonah disappeared beneath the water, so the storm vanished, as if it had been sucked under with him.

The ship sailed on.

But, under the water, an astonishing thing happened.

A great fish lurked under the waters, a colossal beast of the sea, obeying, as all creatures must, the hand of God.

The fish opened its giant mouth and swallowed Jonah alive.

Three days Jonah was in the belly of that dark leviathan, terrified, and shaken with every turn and dive the creature made. From a living death at the depths of the sea Jonah prayed to the Lord, begging pardon and forgiveness.

On the third day the fish opened his mouth. Jonah felt himself pushed with great violence, vomited out of the fish, and thrown onto dry beach sand.

He stood up, trembling. The warm sun beat on his slimy, ragged clothes. Dried seaweed fell from his hair. Soft breezes caressed his arms. Strength came back to his legs.

And then, before he could even open his mouth to thank God, the Voice of the Lord came to him, there on the beach.

"Jonah," said the Voice with infinite gentleness. "Go to Nineveh and preach."

Immediately Jonah obeyed. The fish had placed him halfway there. He journeyed as fast as he could, across the land of

Syria, over the mountains, and ever eastward to the banks of the Tigris, to the city of Nineveh in the land of Assyria.

To the crowds on the streetcorners, to the throngs in the bazaars, Jonah preached as the Lord told him:

"If you do not turn from your evil ways, the city of Nineveh will be destroyed by the Lord in forty days!"

The people believed him. They listened with earnest eyes, and they put on sackcloth, and put ashes on their heads as a sign that they were sorry for their sins. Even the king of Assyria took off his royal robes and dressed in sackcloth and ashes and ordered everyone to fast, and to pray to God to forgive them.

Jonah was amazed, and disappointed. He had not expected the people to listen to him, let alone believe him. He had been the prophet of the Lord, promising destruction to the proudest city then on earth. But God saw that the Assyrians were sorry, and the Voice of the Lord said to Jonah:

"They have turned from their evil ways. The city shall not be destroyed."

When Jonah heard that, he flew into a tantrum of rage. He even talked back to the Lord! He prayed, and said:

"Lord, this is what I knew would happen. You have forgiven them. And You have no right to forgive them. You are a gracious, merciful, kind God, and You forgive evil too easily! These are not Your people. What have You to do with them? Destroy them! If You do not, I beg of You, let me die!"

The Voice of the Lord came like a whisper under Jonah's words: "Jonah—do you think you have a right to be angry?"

And then the Voice was gone.

Jonah gathered up his few belongings, and stomped out of the city, through the deep gates of the mammoth walls. Out on the hills he built himself a shack of dead wood, and

squatted in grim ill-humor, watching to see if the city would
be destroyed.

The sun beat relentlessly on the hill. Jonah's brow was
covered with sweat, and the skin of his face grew red and
blistered. Then, just beside the hut, a vine began to grow.
With amazing swiftness it grew till it shaded Jonah completely, and shielded him from the sun. And Jonah smiled
happily at the vine that made him comfortable.

But, during the night, the Lord sent a worm to eat the
plant, and a piercing east wind to blight it. By sunrise the
plant had shriveled and died. The wind blew a breath like a
furnace on Jonah's head. The sun broiled him with its heat.
Then Jonah cried out:

"It's not fair! There was shade and now the plant died—
I'd rather die than live in heat like this!"

Then the Voice of the Lord said, "Do you do well to be
angry because the vine died?"

Jonah groaned. "I do well to be angry. I have every reason
to be angry!"

But God was patient with this most difficult of all His
prophets, because the lesson Jonah must learn was a lesson
for all men of all time:

"You have pity for the vine. You think it is not fair that
it should die of a worm, yet you did not plant it, or make it
grow. In one night it came up, the next night it died. If you
can pity a vine, how much more should I spare Nineveh,
that great city?"

Then Jonah realized that the Lord was not merely the God
of the Hebrews, but the one true God of all mankind, including the worst heathen.

To stiff-necked, stubborn, grumpy Jonah the Lord had
shown a brand-new thought. The people of Israel were indeed His chosen ones, chosen for a special teaching of His

laws. But the people of all lands, even those who had never yet heard of Him, were His. And He guarded them, and loved them, and saved them. And sometimes they obeyed Him much more quickly than His own prophets!

The
Strange Tale
of
Nebuchadnezzar

Nebuchadnezzar, king of Babylon, awoke from a dream, screaming like a child. He sat up straight in his bed trembling in the morning light. Without combing his hair, without even perfuming his body, he dressed and sent for his court.

"Bring all my wise men here! The magicians, the diviners, the astrologers, everyone!"

When the black-robed peaked-cap wise men stood before him, Nebuchadnezzar said: "I had a terrible dream. You must tell me what it means. For you know and I know that our four thousand gods speak of the future in the dreams of men!"

"Of course," said the peaked-caps, bowing together. "Tell us the dream!"

"I have forgotten the dream, you idiots!" roared Nebuchadnezzar. "I'd tell you if I knew, but it has gone from my head. That is why I called you. You must tell me what it was I dreamed, and then tell me what it means."

The peaked-caps almost fell from the wise men's heads. "Your majesty, no one can tell you what you dreamed!"

"You must tell me what my dream was and what it meant. I will give you great rewards."

The wise men stared at each other, and back at the king. "We cannot possibly do that."

"If you don't—you will die!" screamed Nebuchadnezzar. "I give you one hour!"

At the end of the hour the wise men stood quaking before the throne.

"What you ask is impossible. No man on earth can do it, and no king can ask it. Only the gods themselves could tell you what you actually dreamed."

When Nebuchadnezzar heard that, he flew into a rage. "Issue a royal decree!" he shouted. "Every wise man in the city of Babylon, every wise man in the whole land of Babylonia shall be put to death at once!"

Now, of course, most of the wise men were Babylonians, natives of the country, who had studied in the Temple of the Four Thousand Gods.

But there were in the king's palace four wise men who were not Babylonians, but Jews, men from the kingdom of Judah, who believed in the Lord God of Israel. Their names were Daniel, Shadrach, Meshach, and Abednego, and they were princes of the royal blood of Judah.

They had been brought to Babylon as captives when Nebuchadnezzar destroyed Jerusalem and the Temple of the Lord, which stood there. Nebuchadnezzar had not killed his prisoners as some tyrants do. He had given them land outside Babylon and told them to live there, and build houses, and farm. They were not free to return to their own land, but they were free to live and worship as they pleased in their captivity.

Then Nebuchadnezzar had done a wonderful thing. He had chosen four of the finest young men of Judah, Daniel and the other three, and brought them to the palace to study. Nebuchadnezzar was proud of the learning of his land. The Babylonians worshiped false gods, but they also respected truth as they found it. Their country was an astonishing place, rich with the wonders of engineering and of artistry, governed by a great code of laws, filled with gardens and sculpture, and even libraries where books on carved stone tablets stood on carefully indexed shelves.

Most wonderful of all to the men of Judah were the sciences of Babylon, the amazing accuracy of their medicine, anatomy, and astronomy. Year after year the Babylonians had studied the heavens, charting and naming stars and planets, mapping the skies, learning the secrets of eclipses and comets and falling meteors.

"The stars control us," the Babylonians said. "Our gods made the stars to tell us exactly what will happen tomorrow, and next year, and next century. That is why we study the stars."

Daniel and Shadrach, Meshach and Abednego knew the future was not in the stars. They knew the one true God had made them, not the four thousand gods in Babylon. But they knew too that anyone who studies earnestly the world the Lord made cannot help but learn truth. Soon they too were skilled in astronomy, and in medicine, and in all of Babylonian lore. And because they knew the greatness and glory of the Lord, they understood more than any of the pagan priests.

Nebuchadnezzar had been delighted. "You now know more than any of my wise men, ten times more!" he had said. "You shall live in the palace, and be among my counselors!"

But Daniel and Shadrach, Meshach and Abednego were not in the throne room the morning after the king's dream.

The other wise men, the magicians and the wizards, did not like these foreigners, and did not think it worth while to call them. But when the decree of death went out, soldiers came to arrest Daniel and his three friends, and execute them too.

"Why?" asked Daniel. "Why should good King Nebuchadnezzar do such a cruel thing?"

Brusquely the soldiers explained.

"Wait!" Daniel said. "Let me see the king."

They led him before the throne room. "Nebuchadnezzar," said Daniel, "give me one night. Tomorrow I will tell you about your dream. Till then, let the wise men live!"

Nebuchadnezzar looked at Daniel closely. Since they first met, three years before, when the four men of Judah began their studies, the king had sensed unusual power in the young Jewish prince. "I will do as you ask, Daniel. But if tomorrow you cannot tell me the dream, you shall die with the rest."

All night Daniel, Shadrach, Meshach, and Abednego prayed to the Lord. In the morning sunlight streamed through the prismed windows of the throne room.

"Can you tell me what I dreamed, and what it means?" asked Nebuchadnezzar, one bushy eyebrow raised.

"None of the wise men of Babylon, none of your magicians or astrologers can tell you," said Daniel quietly. "When they wish to learn such secrets they gape at the stars, or slit open the liver of a sheep, and look for bloody signs. The four thousand gods of Babylon cannot help them now."

Daniel flung back his head. His dark hair rippled over his white mantle. "But there is a God in heaven that reveals mysteries, the Lord Who is the One God. He sent you this dream. And He has revealed this to me, His servant, that I might tell it to you."

Daniel stepped closer to the carved steps of the throne.

"In your dream you saw a tall statue. Its head was gold. But its arms and chest were silver. And its stomach and thighs were brass. And its legs were iron. Its feet were part iron, part clay. While you watched in your dream, a rock, cut from a mountain without the use of hands, struck the feet of the statue and broke them in pieces. The whole statue, gold, silver, brass, iron, and clay smashed to bits, and was carried away like dust in the wind. But the stone that hit the statue grew till it became a great mountain and filled the earth."

Nebuchadnezzar stared in dread wonder. "That was my dream!" he whispered hoarsely.

"This is the meaning of it," Daniel continued. "You are a king of kings. And the God of heaven has given you a great kingdom, great power and glory. You are the head of gold. But after you the great kingdoms of the world will grow less and less, shabby and cruel and weak. A kingdom of silver, a kingdom of brass, a kingdom of iron, the one inferior to the other, shall follow. And the day will come when the empires shall be like the feet of the statue, more clay than iron. In those days the God of heaven will set up a kingdom that shall never be destroyed. It shall destroy all other kingdoms, and itself shall stand forever—the Kingdom of God."

Four kingdoms, four empires, did indeed follow Babylon, long after Daniel and Nebuchadnezzar both were dead. Daniel did not name them, but men who study history now can see how his words came true. Babylon, Persia, Greece, and Rome, the four great empires of the world, all fell before the mystic stone of the mountain, the kingdom of Judah and Israel, from which rose the Kingdom of Heaven.

"God sent you the dream that you may know the future. The dream is true, and the interpretation is true," said Daniel.

Nebuchadnezzar rose from his throne, and bowed to the

floor before Daniel as if Daniel were a god himself. Reverence and wonder filled the king's face.

"Truly," said Nebuchadnezzar, "your God is the God of gods, and the Lord of kings, and a revealer of hidden things."

Nebuchadnezzar made Daniel governor over all the provinces of Babylon, and chief of all the wise men in his kingdom. Gifts of gold and jewels he heaped at Daniel's feet.

And Daniel remembered the story of Joseph, the prisoner in Egypt hundreds of years before, who read Pharaoh a dream, and became governor in the land where he had been a slave. The Lord had been with Joseph then. He was with Daniel now.

One more favor Daniel asked. "Let my three friends, Shadrach, Meshach, and Abednego, help me. Let them govern for me out in the provinces. They too are wise in the ways of the Lord our God."

And Nebuchadnezzar agreed.

But Nebuchadnezzar was still a long way from worshiping the Lord! He had been brought up to believe in the four thousand gods of Babylon, and in idols of all kinds. He had also been brought up to believe that these gods had chosen him as king, and that therefore everything he did was right.

As he thought about his dream, he decided that Babylon needed a new idol, a statue of himself, as big and terrible as the one he had seen. So Nebuchadnezzar had his finest sculptors raise a statue of himself ninety feet high, made of pure gold, in the nearby plain of Dura. He called together all the nobles and judges and captains, the rulers and governors and chief men of the provinces, to attend the dedication of the statue. The only important man in the whole country the king did not call was Daniel. Nebuchadnezzar did not say why, and no one dared ask him.

When the glittering crowd of nobles and rulers covered the plain around the statue a herald cried:

"To you it is commanded, to all people, that when you shall hear the sound of the trumpet, and of the flute and the harp and the psaltery, and of the symphony and of all kinds of music, you fall down and adore the golden statue which King Nebuchadnezzar has set up.

"And—if any man shall not fall down and adore, he shall be cast into a furnace of burning fire!"

When the trumpets sounded and the music played, the people fell down and worshiped the golden statue of the king. Hundreds and hundreds of men lay down on their faces in the dirt, and adored the statue as if it were God.

Three men did not bow down. They stood out like three lone trees against the sky—Shadrach, Meshach, and Abednego.

Nebuchadnezzar roared in anger. "Do you refuse to obey my command?"

"We do!"

"Be ready! The trumpet and the music shall sound again, and you may have another chance to bow. And if you do not, you shall burn in the furnace of fire!"

"We do not need another chance," said the three. "We will not worship your gods, nor adore the golden statue you have made. We worship only our God."

Fury blackened Nebuchadnezzar's face: "Heat the furnace seven times hotter than is usual! Let the strongest men of my army tie these men hand and foot, and throw them into the fire!"

The furnace was heated hotter than any fire Babylon had ever seen. Shadrach, Meshach, and Abednego, tied hand and foot, were thrown into the blazing mouth of the furnace, and so hot was the fire that the soldiers who cast them into it were burned to death even though they stood outside!

Down the three men fell, hurtling into the flames in the pit below. Safely above, from a tall tower, Nebuchadnezzar and his court watched the destruction of men who bowed only to the Lord.

But what they saw was not the destruction of three men, but a miracle.

Shadrach, Meshach, and Abednego stood in the center of the furnace, flames leaping around them, and not a hair of their heads nor a thread of their mantles was singed. They walked in the middle of the fire, calm and cool, praising God and blessing the Lord!

The king's servants built the fire higher and higher, with brimstone and pitch and dry sticks, till the flames leaped more than seventy feet into the air. But the angel of the Lord went down with Shadrach, Meshach, and Abednego and drove the fire away, till they stood in an island of cool, dewy wind.

"All ye works of the Lord, bless the Lord," they sang. "Praise and exalt Him above all forever."

Nebuchadnezzar shouted in astonishment. "Did we not throw three men, bound and tied, into the fire?"

"True, O King."

"But I see four men, loose, walking in the midst of the fire, and they are not hurt, and the fourth is like—the Son of God!"

Nebuchadnezzar himself went to the door of the furnace, and shouted into the flames: "Shadrach, Meshach, and Abednego, you servants of the most high God, come out of the fire!"

They came out. The nobles and wise men clustered around them. Everyone could see for themselves that not a hair had been singed, not a thread charred. There was not even the smell of fire about the three of them!

Nebuchadnezzar cried so that all could hear him: "Blessed be the God of Shadrach, Meshach, and Abednego, Who sent His angel and delivered those who believed in Him, and would not adore any god but Him.

"Hear my decree: that every nation and people who shall speak blasphemy against this God shall be destroyed, for there is no other God that can save like this!"

He promoted the three young men to even greater positions, gave them gifts, and went home to his palace in silence.

He did not call for Daniel. He did not want to see Daniel. He was ashamed of what he had done, of the statue and of the furnace, and he wanted to be alone, to ponder the God Whose power he had seen.

Late that night he sat in his curtained chamber. The hourglass had run through four times. The moon shone on the Temple of the Four Thousand Gods of Babylon when the troubled king fell asleep.

Once again Nebuchadnezzar dreamed. This time he did not forget what he saw.

He saw a tree so tall it reached to heaven, and could be seen from all lands. Its leaves were beautiful. It bore much fruit, and every living thing ate from it, and sheltered under its branches. And an angel came down and cried:

"Cut down the tree. Let the beasts and birds run from it. But leave the stump in the earth, and let it be tied with a band of iron and brass, among the grass, and let it be wet with the dew of heaven. And let *his* heart become like a beast's, until seven times pass over him, till the living know that the most High rules in the Kingdom of Heaven."

The wise men could not explain the dream. The soothsayers, the astrologers, the diviners, and the magicians could not explain it. Finally Nebuchadnezzar had to send for Daniel.

"What does it mean?"

Daniel sighed. "You are the tree you saw in the dream, O King. You are powerful and strong, and your power reaches to heaven itself. But you shall be cut down, like the tree. You shall be cast out from among men, and eat grass like an ox, and live among the beasts, till you know that the most High God is the true King. But the stump of the tree will remain, which means your kingdom shall wait for you, till the seven times have passed over you, and you have learned that all power is from heaven."

That is exactly what happened.

Nebuchadnezzar was in his palace, well and happy, when suddenly madness seized him, a strange, fierce, creeping change, terrifying all who saw him. He was driven out of the palace, treated as all insane men of his time were treated, thrown into the wilderness to take care of himself. He ate grass like an ox. His nails grew curved like birds' claws, and his hair grew longer and wilder than eagles' feathers. He crawled on all fours, helpless and abandoned by the men who had called him king.

Then, when the time had come, his sense returned. In a rush happiness surged through him. He lifted his eyes to heaven, and said:

"Bless the name of the Lord, Who lives forever, for His power is an everlasting power, and His kingdom is to all generations!"

Nebuchadnezzar stood again, with a straight back, on two feet, and stretched out his arms, and gloried in the goodness of the Lord, Who had thrown him down and picked him up again.

Back across the wilderness the king walked, a changed

man. Before the threshold of his palace he stopped. There, carved in the step, the same step which today can be seen in the British Museum, were the words:

"For Nebo, the god who blesses me, his temple I have built again."

Nebuchadnezzar threw back his head and laughed, a proud, happy, truly royal laugh.

"Nebo, indeed. I bless the Lord, the one God!"

And he called Daniel and Shadrach, and Meshach and Abednego, and said:

"I brought you to this palace years ago that you could learn all that Babylon had to teach, and I was proud of our learning and our sciences, and I scoffed at you, my prisoners from the little kingdom of Judah.

"Now, I ask you, will you teach me the great glory of Judah? Teach me to worship your God!"

And till the day he died Nebuchadnezzar served the Lord.

Den of
Lions

The prophet named Daniel lived in a tiny room in the back part of the palace. He had scarcely been out of the room for two years. And in that time many things had happened in the kingdom of Babylon.

Daniel was a Jew, a man from the kingdom of Judah, brought to Babylon with all the prisoners of war which King Nebuchadnezzar had taken when he destroyed the city of Jerusalem. Daniel's people still lived in Babylon, exiles and captives, free to do anything except return to their own land. And Daniel, whom the Lord had chosen to prophesy to old King Nebuchadnezzar, and explain the king's dreams, and teach him to serve the Lord instead of the four thousand gods of Babylonia, had lived in the palace a long time. He had seen Nebuchadnezzar's madness, seen his cure, seen the days when Nebuchadnezzar honored the one true God, and seen the day that Nebuchadnezzar had died.

"There's been nothing but trouble since that day," sighed Daniel. "Now we have Belshazzar for a king, and a worse one there's seldom been!"

Daniel paced his little room, thinking. Belshazzar was a pompous, greenish-faced youth, swaggering like a man. He worshiped the gods of Babylon, laughed at the Lord, and spent most of his days looking for new and expensive ways to enjoy himself.

"Danger is here at his doorstep, and Belshazzar refuses to care! He must know his enemies are coming. All the world knows the Medes and Persians are marching great armies of conquest, under Darius the King. And what is Belshazzar doing? Raising an army? Building fortresses? No! He is having a feast!"

The clink of cups, the singing and dancing carried clearly to Daniel's room.

"He is feasting—using the sacred cups stolen from the Temple of the Lord God!"

Years ago, when Nebuchadnezzar destroyed Jerusalem and burned the Lord's Temple to the ground, he had carried the sacred golden vessels from the altars back to Babylon. For years they had rested in the palace treasury, unused, and undefiled.

Belshazzar found them, and chortled with a dazzling idea.

"I will give a feast, and a thousand of my noblemen shall eat and drink from these goblets and trays and dishes. They're gold, fit for a king. They belong to the Lord, the God of Judah? The God old Nebuchadnezzar thought was wonderful? Fine! It will make a good joke to use them. We can all worry deliciously about whether this Lord will punish me!"

King Belshazzar sat in his golden robe under curtains of brocade, making a glutton of himself from the sacred dishes, guzzling from the holy cups. The air was heavy with perfume and the spices of rich foods. Musicians played, singers chanted jubilantly under a shimmering canopy.

Suddenly a breath of cold fear blew through the vast red-draped banquet hall. Whispers rustled, mouth to mouth, like echoes of a gale. The king's face turned waxen in the candle-light, for he was seeing a strange thing, and so were all his thousand frightened guests. It was on the wall.

It was a finger, a finger with joints, but with no hand, a finger in the middle of the air, and it wrote on the wall. Where the finger wrote, words appeared, carved into the stone. It wrote four words, and it disappeared.

The king stood, swaying and shaking, his hands pulling at his black beard, shrieking for his wise men, his astrologers and soothsayers, his magicians.

"What does it mean?"

They hurried forward to stare at the haunted wall, mumbled and shook their heads. They could read the words, but they did not know what they meant.

"Mene, Mene, Tekel, Upharsin."

What could it mean?

The queen stood up, King Belshazzar's mother. "There is a man who can tell us, a Jewish prophet named Daniel. Daniel could read dreams for Nebuchadnezzar when no one else could. Call him!"

Quietly Daniel came into the banquet hall.

"Tell me what those words mean, and I'll give you a purple robe, and a chain of gold, and make you the third prince in the kingdom."

Daniel smiled. "Your rewards are great, but give them to another. I need no price to tell you the meaning of this.

"Your grandfather Nebuchadnezzar was a great king, Bel-shazzar. God gave him riches and power, and then God took them away from him, and sent a madness upon him, to hum-ble his heart and make him realize that everything comes from God, the only real King.

"You knew these things, Belshazzar, but you did not humble your heart before the Lord. You have praised the gods of silver and of gold and of brass, of iron and of wood and of stone, gods that can neither see nor hear nor feel. But the God Who has your breath in His hand, you did not give glory to Him! You have used the gold vessels of His house, the goblets and dishes and cups from the Temple for a feast, to praise your gods.

"Therefore God has written for you to see: *Mene, Mene, Tekel, Upharsin*. Which means: God has numbered your kingdom and finished it. You are weighed in the balance and found wanting. Your kingdom is divided, and given to the Medes and the Persians."

That night the words came true.

Belshazzar the king was killed by the Medes and the Persians. King Darius' armies marched through Babylon's gates, and into the palace. The empire of Babylon, so golden under Nebuchadnezzar, had fallen in the middle of a wicked feast.

King Darius was a world ruler, a great administrator, who knew that he must have other men to govern for him. As a general chooses his captains, so Darius chose his governors to rule the kingdom of Babylon. And over the governors he put three princes, to take care of all the problems the governors had.

Darius chose Daniel to be one of the princes.

"He is a Jew, King Darius, a captive from Judah, and he believes in One he calls the Lord. Why choose him?"

Darius smiled wisely. "He is wise. And Nebuchadnezzar, who was very great, made him a governor here. I will use good men wherever I find them, whoever and whatever they are!"

But the other men in the court were jealous of Daniel, and

tried their best to find something to disgrace him. They could find nothing.

"Every man has a scandal in his past. Every man has sins. But this Daniel seems to have none. And Darius will never get rid of him unless we can prove that he has done something wrong!" they said. "We will have to trick him, somehow!"

"The only thing that means anything to this Daniel is his God," said one plotter, pulling his gray cloak high around his neck. "Listen to me!" And in whispers they wove their plot.

They went to Darius, their eyes gleaming with craftiness under lowered lids.

"King Darius, live forever!" they cried. "We, your governors and princes, ask you to publish a decree, a new law, that for the next thirty days no one may ask a favor of any god or man, except you, O King. Then everyone will know how great you are!"

Darius smiled.

"And," the governors continued, "any man who asks a favor of either, god or man, anyone who prays for the next thirty days, shall be thrown into the den where the wild lions are kept!"

Darius nodded.

"Make it into a law, O King, for all the world knows that a law made by the Medes and Persians can never be changed!"

Darius made it into law, announced through all the land.

Daniel heard it. He knew the law. But the law of the Lord meant more to him. So, as always, three times each day he went to his room, opened the windows which faced the direction of Jerusalem, and gave thanks to God. He did not hide. It was simple to catch Daniel breaking the new law!

They dragged him before Darius the king.

"Daniel has broken your law three times each day, O King! He must be thrown into the den of lions!"

When Darius heard that, tears came to his eyes. He respected Daniel, admired him for his wisdom, and courage, and strength. He did not want Daniel to die! Death by the royal lions was the most terrible of tortures.

"You cannot spare him, you cannot save him," the governors said. "The law of the Medes and the Persians can never be changed."

All day Darius tried to think of some way to save Daniel. He could not. At sunset he said:

"He must be cast into the lions' den!"

They threw Daniel into the cave of the wild lions, hungry beasts who were never fed except when a man was thrown to them to be killed. A stone was shoved in the mouth of the pit, closing it completely. And because the nobles, knowing that Darius did not want Daniel killed, were afraid he might still try to save him, they insisted that the stone be sealed, and marked with the king's own signet ring, and their rings too.

"The way out is sealed! The only other way out is through the jaws of the lions themselves!"

The roaring and the slathering of the lions echoed through the closed entrance. Daniel's enemies went away to rejoice. But King Darius could eat no supper, and, though he went to bed, he could not sleep.

All night lions prowled in his mind, with claws dripping blood, and harsh, drooling tongues and wicked teeth, lions hungry for the kill, and Daniel with no weapon, no shield, no place to hide!

At dawn the king ran to the sealed stone at the mouth of the cave, hoping against hope, certain of what he would find.

"Daniel! Daniel! You who always served the living God!

Can it be, do you think, that your God has been able to save you from the lions?"

Darius the king, emperor, and conqueror of great nations, dropped his head into his hands and sobbed.

But, from the den of the lions, from behind the huge black stone, a voice was calling:

"O King, live forever! My God has sent His angel, and has closed the lions' mouths. They have not hurt me."

Tears shining on his cheeks, Darius called his soldiers to open the den, to lower ladders and ropes, and take Daniel out. And Daniel stood in the sunlight without a scratch on him!

Then King Darius arrested the men who plotted against Daniel, and threw them into the den, and the lions leaped up to catch them in mid-air, and broke their bones between their jaws before their bodies even touched the ground. And Darius sent a letter to all the lands he had conquered saying:

"It is decreed by me, in all my empire, that all men dread and fear the God of Daniel. For He is the living and eternal God. He is the Deliverer and the Savior, doing signs and wonders in heaven and earth, Who has delivered Daniel out of the lions' den!"

And to Daniel God gave many visions, glimpses of the great truths of years to come, visions of the coming of the Son of Man, and of the resurrection on the last day of the world, and of the Judgment, and of everlasting life.

STORIES
FROM
THE NEW TESTAMENT

Mary
and
the Angel

It was spring in Nazareth. Joseph the carpenter closed the door on the clean smell of sawdust and shavings in his shop and walked through the village with a smile on his face. In the sunset the green hillsides glowed with little yellow and crimson anemones. You could even taste the flower sweetness in the wind.

Everywhere around him were noisy happy people, each hurrying about his own business in the twilight. Now and then one of Joseph's customers hailed him—a farmer for whom he had made a plow, a man for whom he had made a table and six benches. Then Joseph turned into a lane, away from the crowds. He was going to the house where Mary lived with Joachim, her father, and Anna, her mother. He had a surprise for all of them.

Ahead of him loomed the white dome of their house. At one side of it a staircase ran to the roof, and looking up there Joseph saw Mary, the beautiful dark-eyed, black-haired girl Joseph loved. She had a lantern in her hand and she was bending over, collecting dates and figs that had been spread out to dry in the hot sun that day. She heard Joseph's footsteps and she straightened up and waved her hand.

Inside the house Anna, like most wives of the village, was busy over a pot of burning coals, preparing to bake fresh loaves of bread. Joachim rose to greet Joseph with a bow, and a smile of welcome.

Joseph seated himself beside the older man. "I have come to ask you if I may marry your daughter, Mary," he said. "I have saved the money I have earned with my hammer and saw. I am ready now to buy all the things we need—a goat, and hens and a rooster. And I love Mary heart and soul. Have I your permission to speak to Mary?"

Joachim nodded solemnly.

Anna looked over her shoulder as she patted the dough into loaves. "I know that you love Mary, and that she loves you. There is no reason to wait," she said. "You may ask Mary."

After supper that night Joseph and Mary walked alone through the damp darkness of the lane, and made their plans. Together under the golden new moon, and the hushed stars, they set the day for their wedding. Within three months they would be married. The night winds smelled of clover and new grass, a night they thought had been specially made to celebrate their happiness.

"This is an evening I shall never forget," said Joseph, as he took Mary's hand to say goodbye.

"Nor will I, Joseph," said Mary, as she watched him turn down the lane back to his carpenter's shop to sleep.

But neither Mary nor Joseph could guess how unforgettable this night would be, nor the tremendous secret that still lay hidden in the shining stars above.

Mary stood at the gate alone for a moment dreaming. Her

mother and father had been sitting up on the roof, talking quietly. The hens and roosters were fast asleep on their perches. The dog was barking behind the garden, and the sheep and goats were dozing.

An ordinary night—*hardly a setting for a miracle!*

Mary smiled and started into the house, her pale blue mantle floating behind her in the breeze. She was expecting nothing more exciting than a good night's sleep. She crossed the lower floor inside the house, and climbed to the inner terrace.

As she went up the steps she realized she was not alone. A tall stranger was standing near the farther wall!

He seemed to stand in light—but there was no lamp there. A kind of silvery mist lay around him, as if the light were his cap and gown. Mary opened her mouth to speak, to ask who he was and what he wanted, but he spoke first.

"Hail, Mary!"

The voice was kind, and deep as the ocean. Mary had never heard a voice like it before, deep and manly, and yet gentle.

"Full of grace!" the voice continued.

Hail, Mary, full of grace! Mary felt shy, and even a little frightened, to have someone speak to her like this.

"The Lord is with you. Blessed are you among women."

Mary folded her hands, and she saw that her hands were shaking, and her arms, and even her shoulders. The stranger also saw she was trembling.

"Do not be afraid, Mary."

She bowed her head. She must not be afraid. She knew she could trust this deep and tender voice. But she could not stop trembling. She closed her eyes and listened to what the stranger was saying. He was telling her that God was greatly pleased with her, and that God was going to give her a baby —a son.

"And you shall call His name Jesus!" said the stranger.

Little thoughts like wild birds darted through Mary's mind. She thought: "Jesus! He will be my son, Jesus. Jesus, son of Mary! I shall have a baby boy, and hold Him in my arms, and sometimes I shall give Him to Joseph to hold, too!"

Yet Mary must listen to the stranger. He was telling her more wonderful things about her son Jesus. He said that Jesus was to have a throne, the throne of the famed king of Israel, King David of history.

"And of all His kingdom, there shall be no end."

Mary listened closely, but still she had not understood the amazing truth that the stranger was trying to tell her. She did not even know who the stranger was, but one question she had to ask him.

"How shall this be done?" she asked in a whisper. "For I am not married."

The stranger stepped nearer and she saw his folded wings, and then she knew him for what he really was, an angel. In the starry fire of his eyes she saw not a frown, but gentle warmth.

His voice grew lower and deeper still:

"The Holy Ghost shall come upon you. The power of the Most High shall overshadow you, and the Holy Child which shall be born of you shall be called—the Son of God."

Mary felt as if she could not breathe, as she heard those words. She would be the mother of a son who would be called the Son of God?

How could one little Nazareth girl take all that in?

The voice of the angel whispered:

"Your cousin Elizabeth . . ."

Mary nodded. She remembered well the day when an angel had told Cousin Elizabeth and Cousin Zachary that they were to have a baby, even though they were old, very old. And indeed what that angel had said came true, for a letter had come from Elizabeth, announcing that she was to have a child.

The angel went on reminding Mary:

"Elizabeth is also to have a son, and she is in her old age! In three months she who never had a child will have a son. Because with God nothing shall be impossible!"

Nothing shall be impossible! Not even for Mary, the girl of sixteen, the girl who tends her father's animals and helps her mother with the baking and the sewing, to have a child who will be the Son of God.

For one instant Mary knew that if she agreed to what the angel said, she would know great sorrow, and pain in the life ahead of her. Things would never again be the same. It was not an easy thing the angel was asking, and Mary knew it, even though she could not then understand all it would mean.

She did not hesitate. She looked up at him, her eyes half closed, her words so soft she could barely hear herself speak.

"Behold, I shall be the handmaid of the Lord. Let it all happen to me, as you have said."

The angel vanished. One instant he was there, gone the next.

Mary crossed the floor and went down on her knees, and then lay on her cot and closed her eyes and wept, and prayed.

Too much for her to understand! She wanted to call out to her mother, to throw herself in her mother's strong arms, and tell her what had happened. But she could not bring herself to tell her secret, just then. They would never believe her. Anna, her mother, and Joachim, her father, still thought of her as a child, anyway.

They would say she had imagined this thing because Cousin Elizabeth was having a child, and Cousin Zachary had said he saw an angel.

Mary lay there quietly while Anna and Joachim tiptoed down from the roof. They went to sleep after their prayers. But Mary could not sleep. She slipped out of bed two hours later. She wrote her mother a note, made herself a bundle of some fresh clothes and a little bread and cheese to eat. She set off alone down the long road.

There was one other person in the world whom she felt she must tell first about her meeting with the angel.

She was walking to Cousin Elizabeth. And as Mary had known, Elizabeth understood the wonderful thing that had happened, and believed it.

Mary stayed with her cousin until Elizabeth's baby was born, the child the angel had said would be called John, the child who grew to be the man we know today as John the Baptist. And as the angel had said, Cousin Zachary who had not been able to speak for nearly a year, found his voice when the baby was born.

"Blessed be the Lord God of Israel!" said Zachary, as he held his son in his arms.

Then Mary went home, and told her mother and her father of the angel who had spoken to her. She told them that she was to have a Son, a baby who would be called Jesus, who would be the Son of God.

And though Mary was afraid they would laugh at her, and tell her she was dreaming, they believed her, for God had whispered in their hearts and told them. And because Anna and Joachim loved her, and Joseph too, they could understand, for that is the way things always are with those who love each other, and love God.

The First
Christmas

In the marble throne room of the palace in Rome, an emperor grinned. His treasury was nearly empty, and he needed more money to spend on his golden chariots and perfumed fountains, on his legions of soldiers and his thousands of slaves. Again and again he had taxed the people of the whole Roman Empire for more gold to be spent on statues of himself, or on gladiators and wild lions for the games in the arena. Still he needed more money. For weeks he had worried and fumed over a way to fill his treasury.

Then suddenly the fat old Emperor Caesar Augustus smiled, and the smile widened to a grin. He had found the answer. He would take a census of his whole empire, count every man, woman, and child in the biggest cities and the smallest towns. Then he would know from whom he could take more money. It was a clever idea, and it made him very happy.

Far away from Rome lay one of his colonies, conquered Palestine, homeland of the Jews. Already Palestine was pay-

ing money to Rome. Every man had to give a tenth of his
corn to the government, and two-tenths of his grapes and
fruit, too. And then there was the poll tax, one per cent from
everybody. And all the other taxes.

But now there were to be even more taxes.

Emperor Caesar Augustus sent a letter to his friend Cyrenus, who was the governor of Syria, and was in charge of
Palestine too. The Emperor ordered Cyrenus to take a census of everyone living in Palestine, to count every Jew in the
country so that no one could escape paying the new tax,
and the Emperor's money vaults would again glitter with
gold.

And in Palestine word of the new census spread through
every street in the little town of Nazareth—and no one in Nazareth liked the idea at all. They had an ancient, proud dislike of being counted. And they had a very modern, very
sensible dislike of paying taxes for the Emperor to waste on
foolishness.

Joseph the carpenter, and Mary his bride, heard the news
most unhappily in their little home behind the carpenter
shop. Any day now, Mary was to have her Baby, the Child
promised by the angel, the boy the angel called the Son of
God. Mary and Joseph had hoped the Baby would be born
at home. They certainly did not want to take a long trip just
before He came!

But Cyrenus the governor had his own notions of how to
take a census. He had sent out orders to every village explaining that to be sure everybody was counted, each person must
pack up and go to the city of the tribe to which he belonged.
Now Joseph belonged to the tribe of King David, and so he
must go all the way down to Bethlehem to be counted.

"Not only you," Joseph was told. "Your wife must also go to
her rightful headquarters to be counted."

"How can Mary go?" he protested. "Don't you know she is going to have a Baby any day?"

But the orders were firm. They must leave at once to be in Bethlehem on the day of the census!

Later Joseph talked with Mary about it. He reminded Mary how long ago Moses had separated the men of Israel into tribes, or houses as they were also called. And ever since families had kept careful records of the tribe to which they belonged. The scrolls of writing in the Nazareth synagogue made it clear that both Joseph and Mary must go to Bethlehem because that was David's city, and they were both of the house of David.

"Why—oh, why—must there be a census—or a trip to Bethlehem?" said Joseph unhappily.

But Mary smiled. "Joseph, my beloved," she said, "remember what the angel said to me?"

"He said, 'Do not be afraid, Mary!'"

"Then," said Mary, "we should not be afraid. And there is something else. I have been listening to the Scriptures in the synagogue, and there are prophecies, Joseph."

"Prophecies about the Messiah, the Savior, the Son of God?"

"Yes. The prophets have said that when the Son of God comes, He will be born in Bethlehem. Had you forgotten, Joseph?"

Joseph gasped.

"Mary, my beloved, we shall go to Bethlehem."

The next morning they began their journey.

From Nazareth it is seventy-five miles to Bethlehem of Judea. Joseph and Mary were not going alone. Mary's mother and father, the kind, strong Anna and Joachim, also had to go and be counted. The two women, Anna and Mary, rode on stubborn little donkeys, while the men trudged alongside and held onto the reins. But donkeys go slowly, and the journey would take them more than three days.

The road was crowded with other families on donkey and on foot. Thousands of people cluttered the highway, all leaving their homes to go and be counted because the Emperor of Rome had said they must. Though they did not like having to go, most of them made a holiday out of the trip. They camped and cooked by the side of the road, and at night pitched tents around wood fires. They slept on blankets spread upon the ground.

During the day they sang their favorite songs, the ones you will find in your Bible called the Psalms of David. Several men had brought along little harps and plucked at the strings, making music as they marched. So it was not a lonely journey and Mary and Joseph were not unhappy.

A shout went up.

"Bethlehem!"

At last they were there, and at last, they thought, they could rest from the long, dusty trip. Joseph took Mary's hand and they looked together at the golden light of a winter sunset slanting on the white houses, and on the hillsides where flocks of sheep were grazing drowsily. This was Bethlehem, where the Son of God was to be born. They looked at each other with silent happiness over their secret.

But as they entered the streets of Bethlehem, Joseph's face wrinkled with worry above his golden beard. The crowds were so great! You could hardly move through the streets because from all over the country the men and women and children of the tribe of David had come to this town to be counted.

Joseph knew he must find a room for Mary at once. The sun was already going, and the night would be cold.

Joseph asked everyone he met to show him the way to an inn, but no one listened. One boy even laughed in his face at such a question.

"Don't you know there are no rooms left in Bethlehem, not even a bed?" taunted the boy as he ran away into the crowd.

Joseph did find five different inns, but they were all filled. He could not understand why no one seemed to care about Mary. He could not understand why there should be no room anywhere for the baby who was coming, the baby who was the Son of God. Even today men and women and children are sometimes so busy thinking of themselves that they cannot make room for the Baby Jesus, even in their hearts.

But Joseph kept on looking. He would not give up. He had to find a room for Mary. At last he found the sixth and last inn in Bethlehem. He shouldered his way through the crowd at the door.

"My wife is about to have a baby," he pleaded. "I must have a bed for her at least."

The innkeeper was a stout and grumpy man with an enormous stomach. He had rolls of fat under his chin, and little dumplings of fat under his eyes, and oily gray curls.

"There is no room," he said. Then he clasped his red hands in front of him and stared at Joseph, at Mary, at Anna and Joachim. Something about them made him stop and think. For a moment he said nothing, then he curled fat fingers around his mouth and bawled:

"Sarah!"

His wife, just as fat as he, came shuffling from the back of the inn.

"What do you want?" She growled at Mary and Joseph. "Don't you realize the town is full? There is not a bed in the town tonight. Still . . ."

The greasy woman turned to her husband.

"There is one place we haven't put anybody yet."

"Is there now? Where? Just where?" demanded the inn-keeper.

Joseph smiled with hope. Perhaps there was a nice, warm, comfortable room waiting for Mary. . . .

"No one's in the stable," said the woman.

"The stable!" said Joseph miserably.

But Mary smiled at the innkeeper's wife. "Thank you," said Mary. "A stable is warm. And it will be a little like home, be-cause often I used to sleep downstairs with the sheep and the goats."

The stable was in a roomy cave under the inn. Joseph held Mary's hand as he led her down twisting stone steps to the floor of earth. The lantern he carried threw strange twisting shadows against the rough walls. As Anna helped Mary to make herself comfortable, Joseph stood apart with Joachim, and wondered.

"I always thought that when Jesus was born, He would come in a great cloud of glory and excitement, with every-thing beautiful around Him. After all, He is God, and King of all. Yet here we are, in a stable, with only donkeys and cows and a dirt floor."

Then suddenly, Joseph and Joachim heard a small clear voice in the stable—a child's first cry.

The Baby was born.

Joseph knelt beside Mary's bed of straw.

"See!" whispered Mary, as she held the Baby. Her Son was wrapped in grandmother Anna's handmade swaddling clothes, the long strips of linen in which all babies then were wrapped.

"Jesus is born!"

The Baby's face was smooth and radiant, and filled with in-nocence and love. This was the Son of God, whom the angel had said would be born to Mary. This was the Savior of the world, the Messiah, whom prophets had promised would come to redeem the world.

And so it was that because an emperor in Rome was greedy for more taxes, the Baby Jesus was born not at home, but in Bethlehem as the ancient holy men had foretold. And because there was no room at the inn, the Child who was the King of Heaven, the Prince of Peace, was born in the poorest place on earth—a stable.

Mary laid Him in a manger, the food box of the donkeys and the cows, which Joseph had cleaned and filled with fresh straw.

The donkeys brayed, and the sheep were bleating, and the warm deep breaths of the cows filled the cave. The stable smelled sweet with the fresh odors of barley and oats and hay. And though it was not the fine palace which Joseph would have liked to offer God as a home, the stable was beautiful on that first Christmas. God had blessed it, and His Son was there.

Shepherds
at the
Back Door

In the crisp darkness of the first Christmas the stable in Bethlehem was silent.

Mary had fallen asleep, wrapped in her long blue mantle. Anna, her mother, and Joachim, her father, had made a bed for themselves far back in the shadows, near the warm breath of the oxen and the sheep. And Jesus, the Baby, lay asleep in His first bed, the manger filled with fresh hay and barley smelling so sweet and clean.

Only Joseph was awake. He could not sleep. He walked quietly around the stable, around and around, stopping regularly to look down at Mary and her Child. Excitement shivered through him, and happiness, and only one thing saddened him, that he had no one to talk to in that dark hour. And so, because he had no one near, he talked to himself, about the wonder of Christmas.

"The odd thing is," he told himself, "that when I looked into that Baby's eyes, I seemed to have known Him all my life. You don't feel that way with most babies. But He—He wasn't a stranger!"

Then Joseph stopped for a minute in his walking.

"One thing," he said to himself, "puzzles me. This Baby is Jesus, the Son of God. The angel told Mary that a long time ago in Nazareth. And yet—we have seen no angels since. There's been nothing but plain ordinary everyday things. Wouldn't you think that when He was born something special would happen? Here's the Baby. Where are the angels?"

Joseph listened, hoping to catch the rustle of an angel's wings, but all he heard was the sleepy bleat of a yearling lamb. And then presently he heard a low rumble of voices in the distance, and the shuffling of feet outside. Then came a knocking at the back stable door.

Joseph hurried to the door, afraid that the knocking would waken Mary. Lifting the latch, he opened the upper half of the door, then put a finger warningly to his mouth. Outside a group of men with bearded faces stared in at him. One man held up a lighted lantern. Behind them the night sky was ablaze with the sparkle of stars, brighter than Joseph ever remembered seeing.

"Peace!" whispered Joseph. "This is no time to make noise."

"The Lord be with you," said one of the men gently. "We have not come to make any trouble at all."

"Who are you then?"

"We are shepherds from the hills outside this town. We have been watching our flocks of sheep."

"The hour is late," said Joseph. He started to close the door on them, but the shepherd who had spoken held up his staff.

"Wait. Only one question we must ask you. Has a Child just been born in this place?"

Joseph drew in his breath, alarmed. Was something wrong, he wondered? Perhaps they had broken a law in sheltering in a stable? No one ever knew what queer laws there might be in these days, between the fat old Emperor in Rome and the ugly King Herod in Jerusalem.

Carefully, Joseph said, "Why do you ask, shepherd? Why is it your business to know if a Child is born here?"

"Don't be afraid of us, man," said the shepherd. "We are friends."

"Well, then," said Joseph. "Yes. A Child has been born here."

"Only a little while ago?" asked the shepherd.

"Yes. In the last two hours."

All the bearded shepherds turned and looked at each other with excitement, and one of them whispered:

"It is true, then."

The shepherd who had spoken before laid a hand on Joseph's shoulder. "Tell me—is it a Boy that is born?"

"It is."

"And tell me, did you put the Baby to sleep in a manger?"

"Yes," answered Joseph. "There was no cradle, you see. The town is so crowded, and there was nowhere else I could take my lady except to this poor stable . . ."

"Then God be praised!" murmured the shepherd, and the others nodded.

"Listen, man," said the one with the lantern. "We five men have just seen a marvelous sight. An unbelievable thing. And it has to do with you!"

"Listen to us," said another. "We were all out on the hillsides tonight, watching over our sheep, minding our own business. The night was clear, air cool, stars bright, everything going along just as usual. We were sitting talking, when suddenly Jonas here interrupted us, and pointed at the sky."

"That I did," said Jonas. "There was a great big bright light in the sky, and it was shaped like an angel bigger than the world. And I heard a voice . . ."

"We all saw the light," declared the first man. "And we all heard the voice from the sky."

"What did the voice say?" asked Joseph eagerly.

"It told us not to be afraid."

"Yes," said Joseph, "the angels always say that first. And then?"

"And then it said it brought us great news. The Savior of the world was being born. I remember the words. How can I ever forget them? The angel said, 'For this day is born to you a Savior who is Christ the Lord.'"

"Christ the Lord," whispered Joseph.

"Yes, friend. That's what the voice said. It told us the Child was being born right here in this town and that we would find Him wrapped in swaddling clothes and lying in a manger."

Another shepherd pushed himself forward.

"You can never imagine what happened then," he broke in excitedly. "The whole heaven seemed to open up. The curtain of stars in the sky flew open, and we saw a host of angels that filled the sky, and they were all singing at the top of their voices . . ."

"And do you know what they were singing?" asked Jonas. "They sang: 'Glory to God in the highest and on earth peace . . .'"

And then the shepherds seemed to lose their tongues. The sound of their own story seemed to quiet them. They were strong, out-of-doors men, not the kind who usually talk of babies and God and of angels in the skies. Suddenly they felt that they must seem foolish.

"Of course," said their leader. "We can't expect you to believe all this."

Then his eyes flashed open, and he looked straight at Joseph. "But it is true," he said. "I saw it. I heard it."

Joseph took his hand. "I believe you," he said.

Then they hurried to tell him how they had left their fat-tailed sheep and run into Bethlehem. Of everyone left on the streets in that midnight hour they had asked questions: Where could they find the new-born Baby? And someone had sent them to the stable of the inn.

The shepherds' tale warmed Joseph's heart. He had been looking for an angel to come to him, some sign that the Son of God was born. But the sign had come to others, which was better. These men, panting and out of breath and sweaty, strong and humble, had seen the gates of heaven open. They had heard singing from on high, the heavens rejoicing at the birth of Mary's Child. Plain, poor working men of the fields were the first to come and visit the newborn Jesus.

Joseph threw back the door to let them in, and received them with open arms. One by one on tiptoe the shepherds followed him and he led them straight to the manger. They looked down and then knelt beside the sleeping Jesus.

Soon they were gone, back to their sheep on the hillsides. Joseph, still wakeful, kept watch over Mary and the Child. In his mind's ear he could hear the countless hosts of heaven singing a message not only for the shepherds, but for all who were ever to live in God's world:

"Peace on earth to men of good will."

Four Kings
and
a Child

In a vast ivory and gold palace on a high hill in Jerusalem lived a king whose name was Herod. Herod was ruler of all Palestine, but no one in the whole land liked him, for his heart was twisted and cruel, and when he grew angry the roar of his voice and the stamping of his boots could be heard far outside the castle walls.

Herod had everything that gold and silver could buy. He had his own musicians and dancing girls and slaves to bring him rare fruits and wine, and to fan him with palm leaves. He had perfumed fountains and a silken couch, and strong white horses, and crowns of rubies. But Herod was never happy. And on this winter day his face scowled darker than the gray-clouded sky.

For weeks he had been hearing strange stories about some special Baby who had been born in Palestine, and the stories worried him. He had heard that some shepherds had seen angels in the sky, and that a holy old man, and an old woman too, had cried out in the Temple that a Baby had been born who would be a Savior for the people.

"What kind of dangerous talk is this? What do they mean, a Savior?" said Herod to himself. "Maybe they mean to make this Baby a king! But I am the king! I can't have such talk going on!"

And so Herod called his soldiers and his spies and told them to try to find this Baby, and learn more about Him. If there really were such a Child called the Prince of Peace, then Herod, the angry king, would destroy Him!

The next day his spies came back with alarming news.

"Three strangers have come to Jerusalem from the East. People say they are kings in disguise. They ride camels, and men call them magi."

"What are magi?" asked Herod.

"Magi are wise men," was the answer. "But these three go around asking questions as if they were not very wise."

"What questions?" growled Herod.

"They are asking about a Child who has just been born— a Child they say will some day be King of Israel. They say they have seen His star in the east and have come to kneel before Him."

"A Child who will be King?" Herod's dark face grew purple with anger, as he stormed up and down the room. "I must find this Child myself—and get rid of Him. He could be very dangerous!"

Suddenly Herod stood still. "Perhaps these wise men can tell me where He is. I shall speak to them, and pretend that I, too, want to kneel before this fabulous Child. Bring them here!"

Before they came, Herod dressed himself in his most kingly robes. He put on his crown of diamonds and rubies, with the tall tuft of rainbow-colored feathers. And then he welcomed them to his throne room.

The three wise men bowed to Herod, and announced their names—Caspar, Melchior, and Balthazar. Tall, keen-eyed they were, these Magi, and one, Herod noted, was black in color, a man from Nubia.

Herod smiled exactly as if nothing at all worried him. "What has brought such great people as you to Palestine?"

"We are following a star," said Caspar, the dark-skinned.

"A star?" repeated Herod. "Then you have seen a star our learned men have not found."

The wise men said nothing.

"Well, at any rate," said Herod, "what do you say this star means?"

The Wise Men were very wise, indeed, because they merely shook their heads, and said they could not tell.

"We simply follow the star."

"But," persisted Herod, "what do you expect to find under this star?"

"A Child," said Balthazar, closing his eyes.

"A Child?" Herod's voice was creamy with interest. "And what about this Child?"

"We cannot say till we find Him," said Melchior.

"Very well, then," growled Herod. "Where do you expect to find Him?"

"Bethlehem!"

"Bethlehem. But it is only a small country place!"

The Wise Men shrugged. "We can only follow the star. To-night we will go on, following it. Where it leads us, we go."

Then Herod had an idea to trap the Wise Men. "Go and find the Child," he said, "and then come back and tell me and I will go and worship Him too."

Herod sent his spies to follow the Wise Men, and find the Child that was born under a magical star. But in the darkness of that night Caspar, Melchior, and Balthazar went by a secret lane to Bethlehem, and the king's spies could not find them to follow them.

The Wise Men found the town and the inn, and the star

led them straight to the stable. They knelt beside the manger, and their eyes were full of love and glory as they gazed upon Mary's baby, Jesus the Son of God.

And then Caspar and Melchior and Balthazar each left a gift by the manger, and bowing, they went out again into the night. Because it was late they went to another inn to sleep, and they planned to go the next day to tell King Herod they had found the Baby. But while they slept they dreamed, all of them the same dream, warning them not to go to Herod, but to go straight away to their own country by a different road. Because of that dream they rose in the middle of the night and mounted their camels and rode away. Herod would never learn from them where Jesus was!

That same night Joseph had a dream, even more strange. An angel came to him and said:

"Get up and take the Child and His mother and go quickly into Egypt, and stay there until I tell you. Because Herod is looking for the Child, hoping to kill Him!"

Joseph leaped from his bed, at once. But how could they go to Egypt? It was many weeks' journey to Egypt. They would need money to travel so far, and he had only a few coins left, because for weeks now he had been away from his work as a carpenter.

What to do?

Through the darkness he saw Joachim, his father-in-law, coming toward him.

"Joseph, I could not sleep. And so I unpacked the gifts the Wise Men left for the Child. Do you know what they brought?"

Joseph shook his head. "I am too worried now, Joachim."

"Look," said Joachim. "Here is frankincense—the most per-

fect perfume of all. And myrrh, the fragrant spice. And here —here is gold!"

"Gold?" Joseph leaned closer to see. "Joachim, it is as if God knew we would need it, and sent it to us, just so we could do what His angel said! Gold for our trip. Listen, Joachim——" And Joseph told the older man of his dream.

In the blackness of night Joseph woke Mary. They said fond goodbyes to Anna and Joachim. Then Joseph put Mary and her Baby on the donkey's back, and tied the bundles of their clothes and goods to the saddle. Staff in one hand, Joseph took the donkey reins with the other, and in the middle of the dark the family started out from Bethlehem. They were taking the road to Egypt.

When King Herod heard that the Wise Men had disappeared without telling him where the Baby was, he screamed with anger.

"I will find that Child—no matter what I must do. I must get rid of Him, that upstart Babe with His angels and His stars!"

And then a horrible idea came to Herod, an idea so terrifying that even he grew pale at the thought. He knew the Child was supposed to be in Bethlehem. And the idea came to this cruel monster of a king that if he killed all the babies in Bethlehem he would be safe from the Child who was the Prince of Peace.

Herod's soldiers went to Bethlehem with swords and spears, and by his orders they killed every boy baby in town. Not one of those holy innocents was spared.

But Herod could not hurt the infant Jesus.

For God had warned Joseph, and Joseph had done just as the angel had said. The holy family was safely on the long road into Egypt.

The Child
Who Was
Not Lost

When Jesus was twelve years old, Mary and Joseph decided to take Him on a visit to Jerusalem to celebrate the wonderful holy springtime feast called the Passover. Every year the family made this journey so they could spend the holy time in the Temple, but this was the first time they would take Jesus with them. Jerusalem was a big city, and if a child should get lost how could anyone hope to find him? Still at twelve a boy is growing up, and can be trusted.

This time Anna and Joachim, His grandmother and grandfather, came with them, and as usual dozens of their friends and relatives from Nazareth with their older children too. The trip was long but gay, and the boys laughed and sang and ran back and forth from one family to another while the little brown donkeys plodded up and down the rocky hillsides. At night they camped by the wayside near a spring of water, and slept under the quivery spring stars.

Just to see the city was excitement enough for the boys. Their mouths gaped at the sight of so many people on the narrow cobbled streets—more people in one street than in all of Nazareth it seemed. Pilgrims came from all over to spend the holiday in Jerusalem, and they heard strange accents, and new languages everywhere they turned.

Jesus had not been to Jerusalem since He was an infant, the day Mary had carried Him into the Temple when He was less than six weeks old. That had been the day when the gnarled old Simeon had crept out of the shadows and called out for all to hear that this Baby was the Savior of the world. And after him had come the aged holy woman named Anna, declaring that Jesus was the Messiah. But Simeon and Anna had both passed away, and now no one in the Temple seemed to remember the words spoken twelve years before. Certainly no one noticed Jesus as He passed by.

With Mary and Joseph the tall young Lad walked into the Temple through the Gate that was called Beautiful. Knotted into the hem of His long white robe Jesus carried a few coins that Joseph had given Him. Mary had shown Him how to tie the copper coins into the cloth so that He would not lose them. With those pennies and mites He paid His own way into the Temple courts.

Joseph had explained to Jesus about money in the Temple. Because the Roman Empire had conquered this land only Roman coins, with a picture of Caesar, could be used for buying and selling. But the Temple was only for the Jews. The Roman Empire had no business there, and so inside the Temple only the old Jewish money could be used.

When people came into the Temple they had with them Roman money. Just inside the gate they changed their Roman silver into Jewish money.

"And," added Joseph sadly, "we always lose money when we do. The money-changers keep some of the money for themselves when they change it. That is how they get rich!"

"Why do people need money in the Temple of God?"

"To buy sacrifices! One must pay for doves and pigeons and lambs to offer them up to God. And you have to pay five times what they are worth," said Joseph.

Jesus listened and said nothing, but He grew very thoughtful.

Jesus and Joseph walked together into the inner parts of the Temple. Mary and Anna went into another part, for the women were not allowed to sit with the men. Jesus looked at the shining altar. There, thirteen years before, Zachary, now dead, had seen an angel and had lost his voice. The boy Jesus counted the twelve steps before the altar, and admired the gilded doorway, and hanging from its gilt rod, the veil of the Temple, a many-colored curtain. Gold spikes on the flat roof glittered in the sunset, and just over the doorway was a gleaming bunch of golden grapes.

Wherever Jesus looked there were priests. The place swarmed with men in ceremonial costume—Levites with pointed caps and large pockets in which they carried the books of the law; Pharisees with deep white fringes on their purple gowns; and with them from Galilee and Judea and the land beyond Jordan crowds of good believers who came to buy lambs or pigeons to offer at the altar. The air was full of the smell of burning offerings, and the smoke of incense.

Jesus heard the voice of the Temple choir and the sounding trumpets. The music of harps softened His dark eyes. He watched the people kneel and pray, and heard the psalms they sang, and they made Him glad.

But why did the people burn the doves and the lambs on the altars? Why did they imagine God would be pleased? Why did the poor have to spend their money to buy animals? Did not such ideas really insult the goodness of the Idea of God?

One of the prophets, Amos, had told the people that God

did not want burnt offerings or feasts—that all He wanted was to see His people just and righteous and good. Yet everyone in the Temple seemed to have forgotten that. It was time they remembered!

Suddenly Jesus stood up, while Joseph still prayed with closed eyes. The Boy strode eagerly into another part of the Temple, and no one saw Him go.

In another part of the Temple sat all the most learned men, who were called Doctors because they were so wise. They knew every word of the Scriptures, and could tell every law that God had made, and they loved God sincerely. But though they knew everything about the laws they did not know much about love, for God or for others. They did not like to talk about how people should live with each other, about honesty and fair play and kindness. They sat in a circle and read the

prophets and argued about what they meant, and their minds were far away from the little problems of everyday life.

Around them sat more men, listening in silence while the Doctors spoke. Not one of them would have dared to interrupt.

Suddenly, without a word of introduction, the twelve-year-old Boy from Nazareth walked into the center of this circle of whitebeards, and slowly began asking questions.

No one knew who He was. They did not even know His name, but something about Him made them listen. At first they were ready to laugh at the idea of a young boy's challenging them. Then, as they listened they grew amazed at all He knew about the Scriptures, and the law, and the prophets. And the questions He asked! They sounded simple, childlike even, and yet they were the wisest and deepest questions ever heard.

Jesus had come to ask them only one thing:

You who are teachers, who are so wise in Scriptures, what do you know of God?

And they did not know that the Boy who asked was Himself the Son of God! They knew only that His tongue seemed on fire with truth, and they found themselves listening to the unknown Child as if they were children, and He the teacher.

They spoke in long, complicated words, and said things they themselves scarcely understood. And Jesus spoke in simple words so that all could understand, as He explained to them that they had forgotten a very important truth. They had forgotten that though God has laws which we must obey, He cares more about what is in our hearts. One kind, good thing we do means more to God than a hundred lambs burnt on an altar, or seventy-seven rules obeyed with no loving smile behind them.

A night passed, and a new day turned into night, and the fifteen men were still trying to answer the Boy no one knew. When the older men grew tired and hungry new Doctors took their places, but Jesus never seemed to need sleep. As another day dawned they still talked, fifteen wise men, and one wiser Boy.

And all the time Jesus kept saying one thing, over and over in different words. Sometimes He would use the words of one of the old prophets, whose name was Micah:

"What does God ask of you, except that you live justly and well, and love kindness, and walk humbly with your God?"

No one noticed how time had sped until Jesus, looking over the heads of the men, saw the pale face of Mary, His mother. Tears were in her eyes. Quietly she spoke to Him:

"Son, why have You done so to us? Your father and I have been looking for You—sorrowing because You were lost."

At once Jesus made His farewell to the Doctors. He

wrapped Mary's blue cloak around her shoulders, and took her hand, and led her toward the gate.

As they walked she told Him what had happened.

"When Joseph finished praying and saw You were gone, he thought You were with Your grandfather, or Your friends, and so he did not worry. And so did I. When we started back to Nazareth we were sure You were with us—maybe with the other boys. But last night we could not find You anywhere."

Mary shook her head sadly at her Son. "You don't know how we wept. How could You run away without a word? How could You treat us like that?"

Jesus looked into His mother's eyes and said with a tender smile:

"Why did you look for Me? Did you not know that I must be about My Father's business?"

And neither Joseph nor Mary could really understand what He said to them. Joseph understood in part. He knew that he was only the foster father of Jesus, and that God was His real Father. So Jesus had been about God's business.

But why had He not told them He must talk with those learned men, instead of letting them think He was lost?

"Perhaps," Mary thought, "it is because even now when He tells us, we do not understand. We never understand all that God does. And remember—this Child is God."

For a moment Mary and Joseph stared at Him, puzzled and worried—but only for that moment, and then suddenly He was their boy again. He hugged His mother, and kissed the gray and golden beard of Joseph.

They need not worry. All the rest of His youth Jesus obeyed them. He went home with them to Nazareth, and Mary watched Him grow into strong manhood as the years passed.

But she never forgot that day in the Temple, nor the words He had spoken to her. She was learning that even those very close to God do not understand the reason for all He does.

What
Happened at
the Wedding

Jesus led His five new followers back to His home in Nazareth. He found His household in a state of excitement and
happy confusion. The daughter of one of Mary's friends was
getting married that very day, and Mary was planning to go
over and help serve the wedding feast.

She was scurrying around the house getting ready when
Jesus and His friends came to the door, without so much as
a word to warn her. Eyes shining, Mary made them all welcome—Peter, Andrew, John, Philip, and Nathanael too. Five
extra men would be a handful in the little home, but whatever Jesus did was right in Mary's eyes. His friends were her
friends, and she made room for them.

"Will you all come to the wedding with me?" she asked.
"The family lives in the village of Cana."

"I come from Cana!" said Nathanael happily.

"Good. Perhaps you will know them. I have promised to
go and help them celebrate," said Mary.

Jesus and His friends were a little tired after walking all

the way from the Jordan to Nazareth, but after they washed
and rested they turned and walked with Mary five miles more
down the road. Near sunset they came into the town of Cana.

Cana was not the most beautiful of towns. It was a jigsaw
jumble of stone houses and huts made out of dried mud. Only
the few well-to-do families had gardens, with cypress trees
and olive groves. The narrow streets were crowded with men
wearing the desert cloak with a hood, the robe we call a bur-
noose. Camels lumbered over the dust and cobblestones.
Women with veiled faces wobbled along perched sideways on
little gray donkeys. Here and there they saw little children
carrying lambs, or playing hide-and-seek among the tents in
the bazaar.

This evening nearly the whole town seemed to be going to
the wedding feast, and the evening air shook with excitement
and music and song. Jesus did not often go to parties of this
kind. He had always been too thoughtful, too studious, to
have time for parties. But tonight He had a happy time. He
and the five disciples put away all thoughts of their serious
talks about God and heaven and how to live, and enjoyed
themselves like everyone else at the feast.

The sound of harps and flutes filled the night, and the
young people danced in their finest clothes. The tables were
covered with the best of meats and fruits, and wine to drink,
and laughter and happiness seemed to bubble around the
beautiful dark-eyed young bride and her tall, black-haired
groom. The family had spared no expense. They had even
hired a caterer, a man whose job it was to provide wine and
food and waiters and dishes and chairs for all the guests, since
no family would ever own enough to take care of such a
crowd. The caterer bustled around busily, and none of the
gay guests noticed that he wore a worried frown.

The fun was at its height when suddenly Mary came to

Jesus, and led Him aside to a corner where no one could over-hear them. Her eyes were troubled.

"They have no more wine," she whispered. "So many peo-ple came, more than they expected—You and Your five friends and many others—and now the wine is about gone, and the party is only just starting. The caterer does not know what to do. There just is no more wine."

Mary smiled. "They are such a nice young couple, and they would be so embarrassed to have to tell their guests they had no more to give them."

Jesus took His mother's hand, and looked into her eyes.

"What is that to Me? And to you? My hour is not yet come," He said.

They were strange words, but Mary knew what He meant. She was asking Him to help this family. Only by a miracle could He help them. There was nowhere to buy wine, now. And Jesus was reminding her that the moment He performed a miracle, the story of it would fly over the land, and every-one would be coming to Him. His time of quiet, and of getting ready would be over. And that would mean taking the first step toward the cross.

Did she really want a miracle now—just so that wedding guests might have more to drink?

Mary knew His thoughts. She knew what a miracle that evening would mean. But she felt so sorry for the young bride and groom, and their family and their guests. She had asked, for their sake. The answer was up to her Son, and she knew He would listen to her plea. Never would He refuse her.

She turned away, and went to the waiters, and told them simply, "Whatever He tells you to do—do it!"

Jesus walked to the back of the room. There He found the six stone water pots which were part of the furnishings of all homes in Palestine, kept there to be used in special religious

purifying ceremonies. With His hand He called the waiters.

"Fill the water pots with water," He said.

They were too polite to let Him see how ridiculous they thought that idea was. Why bother filling pots with water, when what they needed was wine, they wondered? Still, they did as He asked, filling the pots to the brim with clear, fresh water.

"Now take some out of the pots," said Jesus, "and bring it to the caterer."

The waiters dipped a ladle into one pot, and brought it out full. They looked at it and gasped.

"The color has changed!" they shouted. "Look! The water is red!"

"It looks like wine. But it *was* water!"

The caterer heard them shouting and rushed over to see what all the fuss was about. He had been so busy worrying that he had not noticed what went on in the corner. The waiters held the ladle for him to see and taste. With raised eyebrows and a wrinkled nose he sipped it. Then his eyes popped wide open.

"It is fine wine. The finest!"

And the caterer did not know what Jesus had done. The waiters tried to tell him, but he was too busy to listen. He thought the bride's father had been hiding the wine in the water pots, and he hurried over to him at once, a little cross because he had not been told that there was plenty of wine.

"What is happening here?" he asked. "Every man serves the best wine first, at the beginning of the party, and then later when everybody has had some to drink he brings out the wine that is not so good. But you have kept the good wine until now. It is the best I have ever tasted in all my forty years as a caterer in Galilee!"

Soon everybody in the room was talking about the wonderful wine, and finally the waiters made themselves heard, and told how Jesus had changed the water into wine right before their eyes. But when the bride's father and the bride and groom and the guests went to thank Him, Jesus was gone.

He and His disciples were walking back to Nazareth. Because Jesus was silent, His friends did not speak. But in their hearts they marveled at their Master, and because they had seen His first miracle they believed.

The
Rich Man's
Son

In one bedroom of the blue and gold mansion in the seaside town of Capernaum the shutters were closed. Inside on a bed of softest down lay a boy of twelve years, his freckled face crimson with fever. He twisted and tossed on his bed, so sick he seemed not even to know his mother's voice when she spoke to him.

The table by his bed was crowded with medicines, shining bottles of red liquids and jars of black ointment and of gray and green and yellow powders. Four doctors in embroidered robes stood beside him, pulling gravely at their beards.

"Five days and six nights we have watched your son in this illness. We have tried everything," they said. "But we cannot make your son well."

The boy's father, the richest and most powerful man in Capernaum, rose from his seat by the door.

"You *must* make him well. He is my son—and I love him," he said.

"We can do nothing more for him," said the doctors sadly.

The father paced up and down the room, his eyes filling with tears.

"I would spend a fortune to help my boy," he said. "Isn't there any new medicine, or a new doctor you could call?"

"None," said the physicians.

"Somewhere there must be someone who could help!" said the father.

The boy's mother, sitting on the edge of the bed, looked up.

"I have heard of a person named Jesus of Nazareth," she said. "And what I have heard has been strange and wonderful. They say He was just a carpenter but that He has become a great teacher who speaks of God as if He knows Him. Only God can save our child. Could you find this Man called Jesus?"

The father stopped still. "I will find Him," he said.

And so it was that the richest man in Capernaum went alone onto the highways, asking the poorest men he met where he could find the One called Jesus.

Meanwhile, Jesus and His band of five men had left Samaria and started back to Galilee through the sweetness of a May morning. Flocks of storks flew squonking overhead, and land tortoises crept slowly across the road, sure signs that spring had come to Palestine.

Everywhere He went crowds gathered around Jesus to hear Him speak, sometimes on street corners, sometimes in synagogues, or on a farm by the wayside.

"Repent!" He would say, looking into their eyes as if He could see every wrong thing that they had ever done—the lie that man had told, the angry tongue of that woman in green, the penny the little blue-eyed boy had stolen. *Tell God you are sorry*, He was saying, *and ask Him to help you to be good. Love goodness, and turn your back on what you know is wrong.*

"Repent and believe," he said. *Believe that God is good, and that He loves you, and that you must love Him. Believe that God will watch over you, and guard you, and that if you do His will, and live a good life, no evil can hurt you. Believe that though it may be hard to do what God wants, the reward is great, and His help is greater.*

Wherever He went Jesus brought three gifts that could not be seen—the gifts of love, and of hope, and of courage. And the people who heard Him could hardly talk of anything but Jesus. Women, picking beans in the garden, talked of how kind He was to all who came to tell Him their troubles. Farmers in their fields, doing battle against the grasshoppers and locusts who threatened their crops, and hunters in the hills trapping deer and partridge, and the miller, and the hired men, and the traders in the market place all talked about Jesus.

On that gentle May day Jesus and His five disciples stopped to rest by the road not far from Nazareth. Immediately a crowd surrounded them—some to listen, some to stare, and others hoping to tell Jesus their problems, and ask Him what to do. The sun was hot, for it was a little after noon, and there was little shade under the fig trees. And as always in a crowd, the gabble of their voices was enough to make you wish you had no ears.

Then suddenly they fell silent. Down the road and straight through the crowd came a stranger.

The crowd stared at him. They saw his necklace of watery-blue aquamarines, black opals, and grass-green emeralds. They smelled the perfumed oil on his curly hair. Obviously he was a rich man, a nobleman high in the court of King Herod. But why was he on foot, and alone? There was dust

speckled over his fine clothes, and his face was pale, and per-
spiring.

He walked directly up to Jesus. "I have heard strange
stories about You," he said. "I have heard that You make
miracles, that You made a fountain of wine at Cana. And that
at Jacob's well in Samaria You read the secrets of a woman's
mind."

He stopped to catch his breath, then went on, "I need help.
I come from Capernaum. My son is there—very ill. The doctors say he will die. Please—will You come down and heal my
son?"

"Unless you *see* miracles and wonders, you will not believe," replied Jesus, watching the man's face closely.

"Lord—come down before my son dies!" pleaded the father,
and he broke into sobs.

Jesus closed His eyes. Softly He spoke:

"Go your way! Your son lives."

The rich man looked up into Jesus' face, and believed what
He said. His eyes spoke his thanks, and without another word
he turned and ran through the crowd, and raced down the
open road toward Capernaum. And when he left Jesus and
started home it was what was then called the seventh hour of
the day, or what we would call one o'clock in the afternoon.

The road from Nazareth to Capernaum is long. The rich
man ran as far as he could, and then panting for breath he
slowed down to a walk. But he did not stop, not even for a
drink of water. Hour after hour he trudged on through the
dust, hurrying home to his son.

Night came, and he stopped on a stretch of grass for a
few hours' rest.

I believe what Jesus said, he thought to himself as he
watched the moon rise over the hills. Perhaps my friends
would call me a fool to believe the words of an ex-carpenter

from Nazareth—but though He did not say so, I know He is more than that. It is hard to believe, that just by asking Him my son could get well—but I know it is true. Without even seeing the boy, I know it. And he laughed for pure happiness, and scrambled to his feet, and hurried on homeward through the night.

At last by morning light he saw the walls of his home, and outside, waiting for him, were his servants. They ran to greet him.

"Your son is well! The doctors say he will live!"

"Praise God!" said the rich man. "At what hour did he get better?"

"Yesterday, at the seventh hour, the fever left him."

At the seventh hour—one o'clock in the afternoon! The exact moment the father remembered when Jesus had said to him: "Your son lives!"

The father climbed the stairs three at a time, and dashed into his son's room. The bed was empty. The boy, standing by the window, was busy fixing a kite. He looked up and grinned.

"I'm well, father. All well."

"I know. And I must tell you why you are well," said the father.

And so that twelve-year-old boy became the first person in history to hear the amazing truth that if you ask Jesus to help you, and believe that He will, your prayer will be answered. The answer may not come when you expect it, or in the way you expect, but if you believe in Him, He will help you without fail.

"But you must *believe*, heart and soul, and trust Him, without waiting to see His answer first," said the father.

The boy stood straight and tall. "I believe in Jesus—though I have never seen Him. And perhaps somehow I can help others to believe, other children who must learn to love and trust Him without ever seeing Him for themselves."

The Sermon
on
the Mount

Twelve men sat on a mountainside, alone with Jesus. Twelve men who loved Him, and had promised to follow Him, sat in the afternoon sunlight and learned for the first time what it meant to be a Christian.

"Come! Follow Me!" Jesus had said.

They had followed Him into Peter's gray fishing boat, and sailed with Him across the green waters of the Sea of Galilee. At His order they beached the boat on a lonely part of the shore, under the shadow of a towering mountain of black volcanic rock. Up the steep path they climbed till they reached a windflower-lined ledge overlooking the inland sea. Below them the late afternoon fog began to mist over the waters. Over their heads hung the blue sky. It was as though they were on an island of rock, floating between earth and heaven, alone with the Son of God.

An hour before, Jesus had officially chosen these men to be His apostles—messengers, teachers, and soldiers of faith. He had picked them to be the first Christians. And He had brought them to this mountainside to explain what this new faith was, to show them the glories and the hardships, the shining wonders and heavenly mysteries that were to be theirs —and ours.

There on the sunlit ledge He told them all that a soul needs to know of God and the world He has made, of today, and the life to come.

And Jesus was speaking not only to the men who were to be His apostles, but to you, and to me. He was explaining exactly how we should live to please God, whether we are fishermen in Galilee, or businessmen, or children, in this century or the next. The men who heard Him on that afternoon learned His words by heart, and wrote them down for all to read, and treasure. Never have those words been forgotten, though often they are misunderstood.

What does it mean to be a Christian? It means first of all to live in happiness.

Ever since the world was born people have searched for happiness without finding it. They have said: If I had more money, or more of the things money can buy, then I would be happy. They tell themselves that if only they were older, or younger, or stronger, or more beautiful, then certainly they would be happy. And they are wrong. Happiness is found not in getting, but in giving, and in loving God, and following His laws.

Jesus came to offer us happiness. He did not say that we would ever escape pain, or tears, or sickness, or poverty. But He promised that in spite of all those things we could still be happy, and blessed, if we lived as Christians should.

What must we do to be truly happy?

Sitting on the grass, with the soft twilight wind in His hair, Jesus answered that question for His apostles, and for us. He gave us eight rules, which were to be called the Beatitudes, because those who live by them are blessed. And because the One who spoke those rules was the Son of God unchanging, they are as true today as when He spoke on that mountainside so long ago.

"Blessed are the poor in spirit, for theirs is the kingdom of heaven," said Jesus, in His deepest, gentlest voice.

And He meant: Happy are the people who are humble and not proud, who do not boast and brag. A good Christian, He was saying, does not care about riches or fame, or proving how wonderful he is, because he knows that God is more wonderful than anything on this earth.

"Blessed are the meek, for they shall possess the land," said Jesus.

And He meant: If you accept God's will, and believe that because He is good everything He does is good, you will find true happiness. Then nothing that happens to you can frighten you, or make you feel forsaken and alone. A good Christian, He was saying, knows that God loves him, and cares for him, and he feels safe even in the face of darkness and trouble.

"Blessed are they that mourn, for they shall be comforted," said Jesus.

And He meant: You who weep and sorrow for others who are in trouble, and you who help those in need, shall find happiness.

"Blessed are they that hunger and thirst after justice, for they shall have their fill," said Jesus.

And He meant: You who really want to know God, and to know how to serve Him, will surely find happiness, for God will show you His ways, and feed your soul with His love.

"Blessed are the merciful," said Jesus, "for they shall obtain mercy.

"Blessed are the clean of heart—for they shall see God.

"Blessed are the peacemakers, for they shall be called the children of God."

Jesus paused and looked at the twelve men who sat in a circle before Him, men who would soon be killed simply because they served Him. He was about to tell them a startling secret—they would find happiness in suffering, and even in dying for His sake. We may never have to die as they did, but every one of us who are Christians at some time in our lives will suffer a bit for His sake, and His words are true for us as they were for those twelve apostles.

"Blessed are they that suffer persecution for justice's sake, for theirs is the kingdom of heaven.

"Blessed are you when they shall revile you and persecute you, and speak all that is evil against you, untruly, for My sake. Be glad and rejoice, for your reward is very great in heaven!"

The twelve men sat in silence, caught between the gray fog below and the golden light of sunset above. In their hearts His words repeated themselves over, and over—the eight rules of Christian life, so difficult, so simple, so full of the promise of blessed happiness.

Then Jesus spoke again.

Did they remember the Ten Commandments, the laws which God had given Moses so long ago? They did. Then, said Jesus, remember that those laws are important for all Christians, too. But it is not enough to keep from doing evil things, a Christian must not think evil either. And a Christian must be full of love, and kindness, even when it is hardest to love and be kind. To be angry is a sin. To call another a fool, is a sin.

"You have heard it said," Jesus asked, "that you shall love your neighbor and hate your enemy?"

The twelve men nodded. Of course!

Jesus shook His head. "But I say to you: Love your enemies!"

Gently He went on: "Do good to them that hate you. And pray for them that persecute you, and say evil things about you. Remember that you are the children of your Father Who is in heaven, Who makes His sun to rise upon the good, and bad—and His rain to fall upon the just and the unjust."

Quietly, solemnly, He said:

"Be you perfect, as also your heavenly Father is perfect."

Be perfect, He said, but never boast of your perfection.

As the setting sun painted the gray mountain rock with gold and rose light, Jesus explained that a Christian must never be a show-off, especially about his good deeds. If you brag about how kind and generous and loving you are, to make other people admire you, that will be your reward. But if you try to hide your goodness from everyone except God, your reward will come from Him. And, after all, nothing you can find on earth is worth one drop of what you will find in heaven, because the only reason God has created us, and the world we live in, is to let us prepare for a life with Him forever in heaven.

Money? Riches?

Jesus, the King of Heaven who was born in a stable cave, spoke through the twilight:

"Lay not up for yourselves treasures on earth—where rust and moths can consume them, and where thieves break through and steal. But lay up to yourselves treasures in heaven—where neither the rust nor moth can consume, and where thieves do not break through, nor steal.

"For where your treasure is, there is your heart also."

He raised His eyes till He looked far over the heads of His twelve, far over the darkening sea.

"No man can serve two masters. . . . You cannot serve God, and the world with its riches.

"Therefore I say to you, do not think it is important to worry about how you shall find food to eat so that you may live, or how you shall find fine clothes to wear. Is not life more than meat? And the body more than clothes?

"Behold the birds of the air. They do not sow seed, nor reap a harvest, nor gather food into barns. And your heavenly Father feeds them. Are not you of much more value than they? And which of you, by worrying about it, can make yourself even eighteen inches taller?

"And why should you worry about clothing?"

Jesus bent over and touched a brilliant flower growing in the ledge. "Consider the lilies of the field, how they grow. They do not work. They do not spin cloth. But I say to you, that not even King Solomon in all his glory, was dressed as beautifully as one of these. And if God clothes the grass of the field in such glory, how much more richly will He care for you?

"Be not worried, then, saying: What shall we eat? Or what shall we drink? Or with what will we be clothed? Your Father knows you need these things.

"Seek first the kingdom of God, and His justice—and all these things shall be given to you, too."

Jesus rose to His feet, and His tall figure stood out black against the purple evening sky. The last glow of the sunset crowned His hair with golden light, as He spoke the most wonderful promise of all time, the promise that God will answer every prayer.

"Ask—and it shall be given to you.

"Seek, and you shall find.

"Knock, and it shall be opened to you. For every one that

asks, receives. And he that seeks, finds. And to him that knocks, it shall be opened.

"Which man is there among you, who, if his son asks him for bread, would give him a stone? Or if his son asks for a fish to eat, would he give him a serpent?

"If you, who are evil, know how to give good gifts to your children—how much more will your Father Who is in heaven give good things to them that ask Him?"

And now, as darkness settled around them, and night had come, Jesus told His twelve a story. For Jesus was all-wise, and He knew that men remember stories, and understand what they mean, longer than they remember plain words.

"Everyone that hears My words, and obeys them," said Jesus, "is like a wise man who built his house on a rock. And the rain fell and the floods came and the winds blew and they beat upon that house. But that house did not fall, because it was built on a rock.

"And everyone who hears these words of Mine, and does not follow them, shall be like a foolish man that built his house upon the sand. And the rain fell, and the floods came, and the winds blew, and they beat upon that house, and it fell —and great was the fall of it!"

All these things and more Jesus explained to the Twelve as they sat around Him on the mountainside. The stars shone in the sky, and a little crescent moon began to rise as He told them that only by prayers could a man find the strength to live a life like that.

And how should a Christian pray? He should remember that God is his Father and knows what he needs even before he asks. And he should pray like this:

"Our Father, Who art in heaven, hallowed be Thy name.

Thy kingdom come. Thy will be done, on earth as it is in heaven. Give us this day our daily bread. And forgive us our trespasses as we forgive those who trespass against us. And lead us not into temptation, but deliver us from evil . . ."

And the twelve disciples prayed with Him, and the stars shone bright overhead as they learned for the first time the prayer we call the Lord's Prayer.

And that was the Sermon on the Mount, as it was written down for us by Matthew, who had been a publican, but whom we call St. Matthew.

The Story
of the
Prodigal Son

The blue waters of the Sea of Galilee sparkled in the sunlight, and the winds whispered over the shell-strewn shore. In a boat by the beach stood Jesus, leaning on the prow as if it were a pulpit. And on the sand, and the slopes of grass, and even in the branches of the trees above, the crowds sat and listened to Him speak.

The men had left their hammers and their pens and ink, their shops and their farms, to listen. The women had left their dusting and sweeping, and brought their children, to hear Him. They came because they knew He was speaking great truths, and because when He spoke of God, and the mysteries of heaven, they could understand.

Jesus was the greatest teller of good stories the world has ever heard, and the stories He told are called parables. Jesus knew that no one's mind is big enough to understand the God who made us, and so He put God's secrets into stories which we can understand and remember.

The one parable of Jesus that the people remembered best was the adventure of the prodigal son, which means as you know, the son who was wasteful, and threw his money away.

Jesus stood in the swaying bow of the ship, and His eyes twinkled as He began the story.

"A certain man had two sons. . . ."

He was a rich man, this father, who had worked hard to make his farm the finest in the country. He had many acres of land, on which grew good purple grapes, and tall ears of corn, and wheat, and oats and barley. He had fine sleek horses, and big brown-and-white cows to give milk and butter and cheese, white lambs, and a busy flock of chickens. And he had many servants in his house, and hired men in the fields.

Now this rich man had planned that when he died his two sons would inherit the farm and all his money, half for each of them. But the younger son, whom we may call Jacob, did not want to wait. The farm bored him, and he thought that if only he had some money now, and went to the big city, then he could be happy. So he went to his father and said:

"Father, give me my share of the money that will be mine. But give it to me now, while I am still young. I do not want to wait later. And I don't want to stay on this farm all my life!"

The father pulled thoughtfully at his beard, and his gray eyes grew very sad. Ever since his son was a boy he had tried to teach him the good way to live. He had tried to teach him to love God and serve Him, and to be kind and good and wise. And he had tried to make him see that hard work was not only important, but a thing to be proud of, and to enjoy. He had taught his son as best he could, and now his son was a man, and must think for himself, and decide.

"My son would be happier here than in the city, I know," he said to himself. "But if I tell him that he will think I am old and grumpy, and do not understand him. And if I refuse to give him the money, and make him stay here, he will not love me or the farm any better. The only thing to do is let him lead his own life and make his own decisions—and pray that he does not come to harm."

So the father drew out of his chests the money his son asked for, and gave it to him. And a few days later, the son packed his things, and said goodbye to his father and to his brother, and went abroad into a far country to see the world. And as he left the farm he did not even look back to notice the tears in his father's eyes.

"I shall never go back," said the prodigal son. "I'll not be stuck on the farm, working and worrying about sun and rain and drought, the way my father does. Why should I work anyway? I have money. Only stupid fools would work when they already have money. I'm going to spend mine, and have a good time."

So Jacob went abroad with his purse full of gold and silver, and he expected that before long he would become a very great fellow. He was sure that his money would bring him friends and power and even more money, and soon he would be living like a king.

But Jacob was not very wise in the ways of the city. And the wicked men of the city heard the jingle of his purse and rubbed their hands together with glee as they schemed and planned to get the money away from him.

They smiled at Jacob, and put their arms around his shoulders and laughed at his jokes, and pretended to be his friends. They taught him to drink wine, more, far more, than was good for him, and when he had drunk too much and did not know what he was doing, they stole some of his gold.

They taught him how to gamble, and bet large sums of money on a throw of dice or the fall of a card. And because they smiled and winked while they played with him, he never guessed that they were cheating him.

They promised to help him meet all the rich and important people of the city. They told him to give great parties, and they would bring the famous people as guests. So he spent his money on food and wines for the parties, on dancing girls and musicians—but his only guests were the same wicked men and their friends, who were neither rich nor important at all.

In a few months, Jacob's money was all spent. His purse was empty. And when he went to the inns and taverns to find the men who had said they were his friends, they turned their backs on him, and pointed fingers at him and laughed.

A famine came on the land where Jacob was, and all the crops were ruined by bad weather, and there was little food for anyone—especially for a man who had no money and no job. Jacob grew hungry. He walked the streets of the city looking for a job, but no one would hire him.

"What good are you?" laughed the merchants and the shopkeepers and the innkeepers. "What do you know of city life, of buying or selling, or of keeping books? Go back to the country!"

Jacob was weak with hunger, and his cheeks were pale and sunken. His fine city clothes, for which he had spent so much money, were tattered and ragged, and he had to sleep in the streets, or huddled on the steps of a building, because he could not pay for a place to live.

Finally Jacob walked out into the countryside looking for work there. He stopped at the first farm he came to, and knocked at the door.

"Have you any work that I could do?" he asked the farmer. "I am poor, and hungry, but I will take any job."

The farmer looked at the young man and frowned.

"You don't look like you'd be good for much of anything," he said. "But I'll put you to work. You can take care of the pigs—and live with them."

Jacob was so hungry that he took the job, and dirtier, more disgusting work than caring for those swine would be hard to find. He was so hungry that he ate some of the husks which were meant for the pigs' food, because no one would give him anything to eat.

That night, as he made himself a bed of straw in the corner by the pig pen, Jacob never felt lonelier, or closer to tears, even though he was a full-grown man. Alone with the grunting, smelling hogs, he thought to himself:

"Even the hired servants in my father's house have plenty to eat, and here I am nearly dying with hunger. I know that I have been a bad son, and do not even deserve to be called his son any more. But still—I will go to my father and say to him:

"Father, I have sinned against heaven and before you. I have wasted my money, and done many wicked things, and I have been a fool. But even though I am not worthy to be part of your family, will you take me back as one of your servants? For I can learn to work!"

And Jacob got up from his muddy bed, and set off through the night. For more than a week he walked, begging food as he went, and drinking water from the streams, and sleeping in the cold with no blanket under the trees.

Finally he came within sight of his father's farm—and now, what is that that he sees ahead? A hurrying figure coming toward him through the dust!

From far off his father had seen him coming, and ran to greet him, and running to him put his arms around him and kissed him.

"Father," said the prodigal son, "I am sorry. I do not even deserve to be called your son."

The father turned to his servants. "Go quickly and bring a fine robe and put it on him to cover his cold bones, and put a ring on his hand, and shoes on his feet. And go and kill the fatted calf, and roast it. Let us eat and make merry, because this my son was dead to me, and he has come to life again—he was lost and is found!"

Now the older son was out in the fields working, and when he came back to the house he heard music and dancing.

"There is a great feast, because your brother has come home," one of the servants told him.

And when the older son heard that he was so angry he would not even go into the house. His father came out to ask him to join the celebration, but he said to his father:

"This isn't fair. I have served you for years, and obeyed you, and worked hard. And I have never done anything wrong. But you never gave me a feast. Yet look—Jacob goes off and wastes his money gambling and drinking and for him you kill the fatted calf."

His father put his arms around him and held him close. "Son," he said, "you are always with me, and all I have is yours. You know that I love you.

"But your brother who was lost is found, and has turned from his evil ways, and has been saved for us. It is only right that we should rejoice."

And the father and the older son went in and welcomed Jacob, and rejoiced.

And, said Jesus, to His listeners on the beach, God is a Father like that—and we are His children. If we turn from Him, and leave His ways, we will suffer just as did the prodigal son. But like that son, no matter how wicked we have been, we need only to be sorry, and to come back again to God's house, and He will welcome us, and comfort us, and warm us with His love.

God, said Jesus, is a Father, waiting for all His sons to come home.

The Story
of the
Good
Samaritan

"What kind of Man is this Jesus?" snorted a haughty-faced man by the roadside. "He looks like a vagabond, a plain ordinary tramp. Why, He and His apostles spend most of their time walking the highways. If He were as great a teacher as men say, why wouldn't He stay put, and let people come to Him?"

And indeed Jesus and His apostles were not impressive to look at. Their robes were dusty and their feet were calloused and hard, as they trudged along the road.

"Why does your Master travel so much?" asked the man.

Peter answered: "He goes to teach the people, to bring His message to those who cannot come to Him. Our Master is not too proud to go to the poorest house, or the farthest town. Men may be too busy to come to Him, but He is never too busy to come to them!"

On that day in November, when the ruts in the road were frozen hard as carved wood, Jesus led His apostles to a small town called Bethany, in Judea. There they stopped at the home of three old friends of the family, two sisters named Martha and Mary, and Lazarus their brother. And, as He often did, Jesus went to preach in the town synagogue.

The congregation crowded the little house of worship that morning, to hear the words of this famous teacher named Jesus. And as they listened Jesus told them that He promised eternal life to all good people in this world. And what did He mean by eternal life? He meant that even after they died, and their bodies were buried, they would live with God forever in heaven. That was eternal life.

When Jesus said that, everyone was silent wondering. What kind of person was this Who dared to promise eternal life? For they did not know, because He had not told them, that Jesus was the Son of God.

Then one man stood up. He was a lawyer, and he knew the laws of the Scripture by heart. Perhaps, he thought, I can catch this Jesus in a mistake, for He does not look like a man who has studied anywhere near as much as I have!

With a sly look in his left eye, the lawyer said ever so politely: "Master, what must I do to possess eternal life?"

Jesus knew what was in the lawyer's heart. And so He said: "What is written in the law? How do you read it?"

The lawyer blinked. "The law says: You shall love the Lord your God with your whole heart, and with your whole soul, and with all your strength and with all your mind. And you shall love your neighbor as yourself."

And Jesus said: "You have answered rightly. Do this, and you shall live."

But the lawyer did not sit down. "But who *is* my neighbor?" he demanded. "Just which people do I have to love to win eternal life?"

And when he asked that question, the lawyer was hoping to trap Jesus. Because the men to whom Jesus was talking were born Jews, just as Jesus was. And no Jew would have anything to do with the people called Gentiles—or the even worse people called Samaritans.

The lawyer had heard that Jesus had once visited the Samaritans, and eaten with them, and even preached to them. Would He say that even Samaritans were neighbors? That to win eternal life one had to love even such terrible people?

"Master," asked the lawyer raising his eyebrows, "who is my neighbor?"

From where Jesus sat, He could look down the aisle and through the open door to the road beyond, the road that led from Jericho to Jerusalem. That highway was famous as the hiding-place of robbers and thieves, a dangerous place for any traveler. Jesus gazed out at the road, and in answer to the lawyer He began to tell a story, a parable that has never been forgotten.

"*A certain man went down from Jerusalem to Jericho and fell among robbers——*" Jesus began.

And the men listening could see it all in their imaginations as He spoke. They could see that "certain man" packing his bags for the journey, his worried wife helping him and begging him not to go alone, but to wait till he could get someone to go with him. No, no—the business was urgent. He must get to Jericho before dawn tomorrow.

Then his ten-year-old son came to him:

"I know someone going on that road tonight—my friend's father. Why not go with him? He comes from Nablus, and he is a Samaritan, and——"

"What?" roared the father. "What is a son of mine doing playing with a Samaritan boy? Don't you know that no decent person has anything to do with Samaritans?"

"What's wrong with Samaritans, Father?" asked the boy. "My friend is very nice."

"Listen, son," said the father. "Samaritans are all dirty, and they cannot be trusted. Hundreds of years ago they——"

"But Father, what does something that happened hundreds of years ago mean to us? My friend wasn't even alive then!"

"That's enough!" the father said sharply. "No more Samaritan friends for you. No son of mine may be seen playing with a Samaritan. Do you understand that? And tonight I shall go alone to Jericho."

The father started out on the dark road, alone, and when he was far from town thieves overtook him, and took not only his money, but all his clothes. They left him naked on the ground in the dark—beaten, wounded, and half dead.

And now the crowd was very still as Jesus told them:

"And it chanced that a certain priest went down the same way, and saw him, and passed by.

"And in the same way a Levite when he was near the place and saw him, passed by.

"But a certain Samaritan, being on his journey, came near him, and seeing him took pity on him."

And the Samaritan did not pass by. He knew it was dangerous to stop on the road for anything, and he too was in a hurry just as the others had been. But still, he stopped.

He went over to the wounded man, and bandaged him, pouring oil and wine into the deep cuts left by the robbers' knives, and tying them up with clean strips of cloth. Then he picked the man up, and put him on his own horse, and brought him to an inn, and took care of him.

And the next day, when the Samaritan had to leave, the wounded man was still not well enough to travel. So the Samaritan took money out of his own purse and gave it to the innkeeper, and said:

"Take care of him, and whatever more you may need to spend, I will repay you when I return."

And without even waiting for thanks the Samaritan went on his way.

Jesus paused and looked from the faces of the people straight at the lawyer.

"Which of these three men—the priest, the Levite, or the Samaritan—was a neighbor to the man that fell among the the robbers?"

And looking back into the smiling face of the Master the lawyer could answer only:

"He that showed mercy to him." And he meant, the Samaritan.

And Jesus said to him: *"Go, and do you in like manner!"*

The men and women of Bethany never forgot the story of the Good Samaritan. And even today, wherever it is told, men remember that when God says He wants us to love our neighbors He means for us to love everyone, and hate and despise no one.

The Daughter
of
Jairus

The man named Jairus paced up and down the marble floor
of the downstairs room of his house.

"Are the doctors still in there?" he asked in a voice so low
it could hardly be heard over the sound of his sandals. "Will
they never come out and tell me how Joanna is?"

His friend put an arm on Jairus' shoulder. "Jairus, sit down
and rest. Since your daughter became ill you have not rested.
The doctors are trying their best to make her well. And you
must wait, and have patience, and take care of yourself.
What else can you do?"

Jairus raised tear-stained eyes to meet his friend's gaze.

"My little girl is sick, dangerously sick, and you ask me
what I can do? I can get her the best doctors—and that I have
done. And because I am head of the synagogue, and love my
God, I can pray. I have prayed night and day that He would
make her well. And if doctors and prayers do not work, I
know what I shall do."

"What more can you do, Jairus?"

"I shall go to Jesus, and ask Him to save her," said Jairus.

His friend's eyes opened wide with surprise. "Do you, the head of the synagogue, such a wise and important person as you, believe in this Jesus of Nazareth?"

"I do," said Jairus. "He has helped many. Perhaps He will help Joanna. And why should it surprise you that I believe in Him? He is wiser, and far more important than I, and He speaks with surer knowledge than I."

"Men will call you foolish to go to Jesus—a carpenter turned preacher, a poor Man who wanders the roads like a vagabond!" said his friend. "Don't go to Him!"

Slow footsteps echoed on the stairs. Jairus turned as the three doctors came into the room, carrying their scarlet and green bags of medicines and powders. The oldest doctor, whose face was gray and wrinkled as desert rock, put his hands on Jairus' shoulders.

"Jairus, there is nothing more that we can do. Your daughter—Joanna is dying."

Jairus stared at the doctor, and his cheeks went pale. Then without a word, he shook off the doctor's hands, and ran out of the house.

"Where has he gone?" asked the doctor.

"He has gone to see the One called Jesus," said his friend.

"Fool!" said the doctor. "What can Jesus do that we cannot?"

"Have you seen Jesus?" asked Jairus of the washerwoman by the town well.

"He is down by the shore," the woman said. "I'm on my way there soon."

But Jairus could not wait. He ran through the streets and down the hills, his sandals flapping, and his brown and orange robes streaming out in the breeze. And as he ran he thought of Joanna, the little girl he loved so dearly, the twelve-year-old with the black eyes who liked to sing and to play house under the tree in the back yard. Why would God want her to die? What possible reason could there be for a pink-cheeked little girl to die?

At last Jairus reached the beach. A thick crowd surrounded Jesus, but Jairus pushed and pleaded and squirmed his way through, and when he saw the Master, Jairus fell on his knees by Jesus' feet.

"My daughter is at the point of death," he said. "Come— and just lay Your hand on her—and then she will be safe, and will live. Please, Lord—come."

With His strong hands Jesus helped Jairus to stand, and rose Himself to go with him to his house. But the crowds followed Him through the streets, pushing and jostling and elbowing each other to get closer to Jesus. And there was in the crowd a woman who had been sick for twelve years, with a wound that never stopped bleeding. And she said to herself, "If I can only get close enough to touch Jesus' robe, that alone would make me well." Sick as she was, she made her way through the crowd.

Suddenly Jesus stopped. "Who touched Me?" He asked.

The apostles looked at Him and laughed. "Is this some kind of joke, Master?" asked Philip. "Look at the crowds all around you. How can You ask which person touched You?"

But Jesus did not even smile. He turned and looked behind Him, and from out of the crowd came the woman, and kneeling before Him she said:

"Lord, I touched Your robe, and I knew if I did, You could heal me. And see, I am made well again!"

Jesus put a hand in blessing on her head. "Daughter," He said, "it is your faith that has made you well. Go in peace."

Jairus stood silent beside Jesus. He did not dare say anything, but to himself he was thinking: Why, oh why, must He heal this woman now? If we don't hurry it will be too late to save Joanna!

And then Jairus saw his friend and the doctors shouldering their way through the crowd.

"Jairus," said his friend. "Your daughter is dead. Why trouble the Master any more? It is too late, now."

But Jesus heard what the man had said, and He turned to Jairus, and put His arm around him. And Jesus whispered:

"Fear not. Only—*believe!*"

And with His arm firmly around Jairus, Jesus walked with him up the streets until they came to Jairus' house. A crowd came with them—but there was already another large throng at the house. All Jairus' relatives and his friends from the synagogue had arrived. Joanna's aunts and uncles, and grandparents, and all her friends, and all who had known and loved the laughing little girl were there, weeping and crying because she was dead.

Jesus waved His hand at the crowd who had followed Him to stay back. Only Peter and John and James—and Jairus—could go in with Him.

On the doorstep, Jesus spoke to the men and women and children who were weeping for Joanna.

"Why are you making this ado, and weeping?" He asked gently. "The little girl is not dead. She only sleeps!"

And the family and friends stared at the tall Man in the white robe, and laughed at Him through their tears, and yelled at Him, and tried to put Him out. They knew that Joanna was truly dead, and the words of Jesus sounded to them cruel, and strange, because they did not believe in Him.

But Jesus went inside the house, with Peter and James and John and Jairus. He went to Joanna's mother, and wiped her tears. He took her arm and led them all upstairs to the darkened room where the child lay, white and motionless.

Jesus bent over the bed. He lifted up one cold, limp hand, and murmured:

"Little girl, arise!"

And as He spoke, Joanna opened her eyes, and stretched, and got out of bed, and walked straight into her mother's and father's arms.

"She is alive. She was dead and she lives! O Lord, thank You!" said Jairus, as he held her close.

Tears of joy streamed down the mother's cheeks, as she stared open-mouthed at Jesus, and fell to her knees before Him to adore Him.

Jesus, with the most pleased and tender and understanding smile, leaned down to look in Joanna's eyes.

"Give her something to eat," He said gently. Any little girl called back from death to life would probably be hungry.

Jesus straightened up to His full height, and His bearded face grew solemn. One more thing, He said: *Tell no one what has happened here.*

For one last instant Jesus laid His hand on Joanna's black curls, then taking Peter and James and John with Him, He went silently down the stairs, and past the weeping aunts and uncles and friends, and out the door of Jairus' house. And the crowd who had waited for Him, followed Him back to the beach.

Joanna's mother hurried off to fix her some fresh bread and butter, and a cup of bubbly cold milk. Downstairs the relatives and friends who had been weeping were noisy with questions.

"What happened? Is she really alive now? Did Jesus really bring her back from death? Tell us! Tell us!" they gabbled. "You look so happy, something fine must have happened."

But Joanna's mother only smiled and said nothing, as Jesus had commanded. These were the people who had laughed at Him, and who had not believed when He came. Let them wonder now. Let them ask and get no answer. For Jesus had no use for those who could not believe.

And upstairs, holding his daughter close, Jairus whispered:

"My dearest daughter, no matter what happens in your life, always believe."

He held her chin in his hands. "Sometimes," he said, "you will wonder why God lets terrible things happen—why He does not hurry to answer your prayers. And sometimes you will not understand Him at all. But always you must trust Him, and believe, even when His answer to your prayer is No."

Jairus hugged her close.

"Remember, what Jesus said to me. He said 'Fear not. Only *believe.*'"

And Joanna repeated the great secret of Jesus:

"Fear not. Only *believe!*"

And though Jairus and his wife and Joanna obeyed Jesus and never told anyone what happened, the story spread faster than sunrise. The doctors, the relatives, the friends who had seen her die, saw Joanna alive again, laughing and singing, and growing to be a beautiful woman. And they who saw her told everyone they knew about the miracle, and eventually it was written down for us by St. Matthew, and St. Mark and St. Luke so that we could share the secret Joanna had learned from the Lord.

The Boy
with the
Five Loaves

Jesus and His disciples had gone away.

For long hours they had preached, and healed the sick, without stopping even to eat. At last they could give no more. With the Master they climbed into Peter's boat and sailed across the Sea of Galilee to a deserted part of the shore, far from any town, hoping to find silence, and rest, and peace for prayer.

But some in the crowd had overheard the apostles' plans, and they told others. The wind had barely begun to fill Peter's sails when the crowd started down the beach on foot, determined to meet Jesus on the other side of the sea. They forgot He needed rest. They knew only that they needed Him, and that He would never turn them away.

They put their sick relatives and friends on litters and stretchers, ready to carry them four times around the sea if only the Master would heal them. They slung their babies on their shoulders. They grabbed handfuls of fruit and nuts to munch along the way. They called to their neighbors and to people on the streets to join them. And singing and laughing they started the long walk to the place where they knew Peter planned to put his boat ashore.

"Drop what you're doing and come," they called. "Come quickly, before it is too late!"

A little boy in a faded brown robe was perched on the edge of the town well when he heard that call. Quicker than a field mouse he darted home, and burst into the kitchen. His mother was pulling sweet-smelling loaves of new-baked bread from the oven.

"Can I go too, Mother? Huh? Can I go?"

Hands on her hips, she looked at him. "Well, Seth, you are a big boy of eleven now. Yes, you may go. But stay close to the others, and don't get lost. And—you must take some food."

"Oh, Mother! No!" Seth protested, but in vain.

"I'll be too late," he said, as his mother wrapped two freshly baked fish in cool green leaves and placed them in a basket.

"No one else is taking food. I'll look like a baby," he wailed. And then: "That's too much to carry, and too much for me to eat!"

His mother wrapped five loaves of new barley bread in clean muslin and packed them in the basket.

"No son of mine will go anywhere without some food, not even to follow the Master, so long as I am here to prepare it. And you will take more than you need, Seth, to have some to share if the others bring none. That surely is what the Master would tell you to do."

She kissed him on the forehead. "I have a feeling you will be glad you waited for this," she said. "Have a good time! And Seth—don't lose that basket!"

"I won't." Seth turned and ran down the path, through the

streets, and down to the beach, as fast as his sandals could carry him. But the crowds were already almost out of sight around the curving shore of the lake. Their laughter and singing echoed over the gentle waves.

"If I hadn't had to wait for this basket," grumbled Seth, "I'd be with them now. Of all the stupid things, having to carry a lunch!"

He tried singing to himself as he hurried over the sand, but his voice was thin and his breath came hard, so he stopped. The basket was heavy, and the handle pressed into his fingers. He switched it to the other hand.

"It's lonesome walking alone like this," Seth said out loud. "I could stop, right here. I don't have to go to hear Jesus. I've heard Him before."

Then he answered himself. "Why should I stop? I want to go to Jesus. Wherever He is. Don't ask me why——" he said to a bird wheeling overhead. "I don't know enough to tell you in words. But I know inside me."

Seth looked around to be sure no one else had overheard him. And he threw back his shoulders and held his chin high, and strode along the way his father did when they walked together.

But the basket was heavy, and awkward. It bumped against his legs. And the sun was higher now, and hot. Prickles of sweat started on his neck.

"I could hide the basket, and pick it up on the way home," he said to himself. But suppose some wanderer found it, and stole it? Seth clenched his lips and walked on.

"I could say I lost it," he thought, kicking at the pebbles. "I could go so fast without it!" For a moment he put it down. Then he picked it up with the other hand. He had promised his mother. And besides, why bother to go to Jesus if you were already planning a lie in your heart?

His hair fell over his eyes, and stuck damply to his cheeks. His feet hurt, and the basket grew heavier every second. He walked on, past the great black boulder, around a shining blue inlet, up over the dunes. He walked and walked. Noon had passed, and the heat rising from the white sand was blinding.

Seth dropped the basket to the ground, and watched it wobble and teeter till it came to rest at a crooked angle against the gray and brown rocks. He straightened his fingers and studied the four whitish blisters that had risen on his palm. His stomach rumbled and gurgled with hunger.

"I could eat some now," he said to the waves, "and the basket would be lighter, and easier to carry."

Then he shook his head in answer. "Mother gave me the food to share. So I should wait till I get there. I'll be hungrier then, anyway. Wonder how far it is now?" Even though no one else could hear him, Seth made his voice sound strong and brave, because listening to it made him feel better!

He squinched his eyes and peered down the beach. Far off he could see where the crowd had stopped—and there by the shore was a swaying black dot that must be Peter's boat.

"They found Him!" said Seth to the wind. "If I hurry I can get there in an hour or so."

Rescuing the basket, he started off again. But he could not keep his eyes on the spot where Jesus was. He must watch where he walked, careful of stones and scrub pine, and vines to trip over. His nose itched. His legs were so tired the calves of them twitched. His sandal straps rubbed at his heels. And suddenly he was lonely, more lonely than in all his eleven years of life, and here where no one could see him, Seth came very close to tears.

He lost track of time. He simply walked. An hour passed. Another. Perspiration and tears stung his eyes and cheeks.

Angrily he rubbed his eyes with his fist, and walked. . . .

The sun was low over the sea when Seth finally saw Jesus. He saw no one else. Without thinking he walked right through the crowds up to the very front row of the giant circle of faces around the Master. With a sigh he sank to his knees on the grass, and laid his hand on the basket lid. Jesus was speaking, and His words flowed over Seth like a cool breeze, smoothing his cheek, caressing his hair. For once Seth did not listen to the words themselves. He heard only the love in Jesus' voice. Eyes closed, Seth listened, and understood with his heart.

The sun sank steadily over the sea. The sky purpled with twilight. The first star shone in the west. And Jesus' voice fell silent.

Seth opened his eyes. Not twelve feet from him the apostles huddled around the Master, their faces grave. Seth heard Philip say:

"Lord, this is a desert place, and the dinner hour has already passed. Send these people away now, so that they can go to the next villages and towns and buy themselves meat to eat."

Seth's eyes widened, as he heard Jesus reply: "They have no need to go. *Give* them something to eat!"

And Philip gazing out at the crowd said shyly to his Master, "Lord—two hundred pence would not buy enough food for all these!"

Seth scrambled to his feet. Taking his basket, he ran to the nearest apostle, the fisherman named Andrew.

"I have some food," he said. "Not much. But take it! I'm— I'm not hungry. My mother made me bring this."

Andrew bent down and grasped Seth's shoulders with a welcoming smile. "Do you realize you're the only person here with any food at all? My brother, Peter, and the rest of us went and asked everyone. Not even a fig left in the whole crowd!"

Andrew peered at Seth's dirt-smeared face. He saw the streaks of dried sweat, and the tangled hair, and the blisters on his palm. "You worked hard to carry that food. Who knows? You may not know what you have done. Come!"

With his hand firmly on Seth's shoulder, Andrew led him straight to Jesus. "Lord," said the apostle, "there is a boy here who has five loaves of barley bread, and two fishes." Andrew paused, then added lamely. "But—what are these among so many?"

Jesus looked at Seth, and the dark eyes of the Son of God seemed to brighten the twilight with their smile. Those eyes seemed to Seth to be looking into the corners of his heart, and to be pleased, and to say a silent: "Well done!"

Then Jesus said to Andrew and the others: "Make the men sit down!" For many people, seeing that night had overtaken them and that Jesus had stopped preaching, were already preparing to start the long walk home. The apostles went out among the crowd, urging them to stay, and telling them to sit on the grass in rows of fifty and a hundred by families. Then the apostles counted, to see how many must be fed.

"Lord," said Peter at last, "there are five thousand men— and their wives and children, too. Five thousand!"

For answer Jesus unwrapped Seth's five loaves of bread. Standing, He took the bread and raised it toward heaven, and gave thanks to God, and blessed it. Then he broke the loaves into pieces, and began giving them to the apostles to feed the crowd. Then He took the two baked fish from their wrapper of leaves, and gave thanks again, and blessed them, too, and broke them in pieces.

Seth sucked his cheeks in silent wonder.

At first the apostles took the pieces of bread and fish in their hands to give away. But their hands could not hold all the pieces! One by one they scurried off to get baskets, their eyes wide with astonishment.

At the touch of Jesus the bread and fish seemed to multiply, and grow. Piece after piece the Lord broke off, and still the food was not gone. Andrew and Philip and Peter hurried off with full baskets, and the others of the twelve as well, and when they came back Jesus filled them again and again. Row after row of people, hundreds after hundreds, ate of those five loaves and two fishes. There were even second helpings for those who needed more!

Andrew had given Seth his share immediately but Seth held it, waiting to see if there would really be enough for everyone. An hour passed, and the five thousand ate their fill, and the apostles, and even Jesus. And in the growing darkness, Seth ate too.

Andrew came and sat beside him on the cool grass. "Do you know what you have done?" whispered Andrew.

"I have seen a miracle," said Seth. "That I know."

"You have helped to make a miracle," Andrew said. "Your mother and you. I do not know what it cost you in trouble and pain and weariness, but He knows. And look what He has made of the little you offered!"

Then the voice of Jesus sounded quietly as He spoke to the apostles: "Gather up the pieces that remain, lest they be lost!"

Seth whispered in Andrew's ear. "Why should He bother with the leftovers, when by a miracle He can feed thousands?"

Andrew smiled. "Even God does not waste His gifts. Neither should we!" And rising to his feet he went with the others, to gather the pieces. When they were through, the fragments of bread filled twelve baskets. More remained than Seth had brought!

From the crowd came a murmur. And the murmur grew to a rumbling, and the rumbling to a roar.

"This is in truth the prophet we have been promised! This Jesus is the Messiah!"

And suddenly, the crowd was moving toward Jesus crying: "Lord, be our King!" "A King!"

Seth craned his neck to see the face of Jesus. The Master stood shaking His head in gentleness, and even sadness, as the crowd approached. Not for a king's crown had He come to the world!

With outstretched arms Jesus tried to stop them, these miracle-filled men who did not yet understand the Kingdom of God. He turned to His apostles, and gave them orders: they were to get into Peter's boat and sail home without Him.

Then, leaving the puzzled crowd behind Him, Jesus turned and hurried up the mountainside alone to pray.

Seth also walked alone that night. There were people all around him, talking as they made the long journey home around the beach. But Seth, his empty basket swinging at his side, hardly heard them. In the light of the torches he saw only the eyes of Jesus as they had looked at him and smiled.

"Why did He not want to be King?" he wondered. "I have heard Him speak of the kingdom of heaven, but I do not know what He means. All I know is that He is *my* King. And I shall love Him, and honor Him, and obey His word till I die."

And hugging the secret of the miracle to his heart, Seth hurried homeward to tell his mother of the wonders that had been done, the wonder God had made from her five loaves of new barley bread, and her two fresh-baked fish.

"Little Children!"

"The kingdom of heaven!" said John slowly. He lay under the gold and gray shadows of the fig tree, his eyes closed in a daydream.

Around him the others of the twelve apostles sat, some leaning against the trunk, some tailor-fashion, some with their bearded chins in their hands. This day they were to take to the road again, walking back to Jerusalem with the Master. They were only waiting for Jesus Himself to be ready. Till then, they sat in Peter's front yard, grateful for a moment's idleness.

"I wonder what His kingdom will be like," said John. "Will there be crowns? And thrones?"

"Don't you remember?" asked Nathanael Bartholomew. "He told us His kingdom was not of this world."

"He doesn't want to be a king," said Judas Iscariot bitterly. "He ran away the time the crowd tried to make Him one."

"Well, whatever it's like," said John smugly, "I guess I'll have an important place in it."

"I suppose you think you'll be sitting at the Lord's right

hand," said his brother, James, chewing on a blade of grass.

"Could well be," said John, opening his eyes.

James sat up. "If anybody will, I will!"

Jude Thaddeus laughed. "I guess since the other James and Simon and I are His own cousins, we should come before you!"

And in no time at all, Peter's front yard was as full of squabbling and bickering as a hen house. Grown men these were, and the closest followers of Jesus, yet they argued and grew red in the face, and snapped at each other, each insisting he would be the most important one in the kingdom of God.

Finally Peter stood up and raised his hand for silence. "Look here!" he said. "None of us knows what Jesus means by His kingdom. How can we know where we will stand in it? At the right time, we will ask Him."

When the Master came out of the house they followed Him in silence as He led the way out of the gate and into the street.

"Master——" began John, but he did not finish. From every doorway men and women of Capernaum came running to see Jesus, to wave to Him, to call to Him, and bid Him a good journey.

"Lord——" began James, but he too was interrupted. People swarmed around the Master, asking His blessing, and shouting farewells.

Slowly, smilingly, Jesus made His way through the throngs. At one street corner the crowd thinned for an instant, and the disciples could keep silent no longer. Tugging at His sleeve they asked:

"Master! Who do You think will be the greatest in the kingdom of heaven? Which one of us?"

Jesus stopped and looked at His apostles, and sadness dark-

ened His eyes. He seemed to say: *Do you still not understand?*

Then bending down He singled out one child from the
crowd, a little fellow of six years, with twinkling brown eyes
and thick unruly hair.

"Come to Me!" He said, and held out His arms. The boy
ran to Him, and Jesus cleared a space for Him in the crowd,
and held him where all could see.

"In truth I say to you—unless you become as little children,
you shall not enter into the kingdom of heaven!" said Jesus.

"And he that receives one such a little child in My name,"
Jesus continued, "receives Me. But he that shall scandalize
one of these little ones that believe in Me, it were better for
him that a millstone should be hung around his neck and that
he should be drowned in the depths of the sea!"

The apostles looked at each other with dismay. *Children
were wonderful, that is true!,* they thought to themselves. *But
to become like a little child? It sounded ridiculous. They were
grown men, proud of their wisdom and their knowledge. And
this chubby-cheeked boy—what could he know that they did
not?*

Jesus read their thoughts, and a warning flashed in His
eyes.

"See that you despise not one of these little ones! For I say
to you that their angels in heaven always see the face of My
Father, who is in heaven."

Then Jesus rose, His hand still caressing the boy's shock of
unruly hair. Sadly but firmly He answered His apostles' question.

"If any man desires to be first—he shall be the last of all!"

The mothers and fathers of Capernaum had listened spellbound to His words. True, they had always seen that the

Master enjoyed children. They had seen Him swing them up to His shoulder, seen Him whittle whistles and doll beds for them, watched Him as He gathered them round Him at twilight to hear His stories of the secret ways of God.

But He loved them! Hear what He said—that you must become like a child to enter His kingdom. No man in history, plain teacher or prophet, ever spoke so wondrously about children, save Jesus!

And mothers and fathers pressed toward Him now, bringing their children to Him. Girls and boys they came, ragamuffins and those dressed in finest woolens, fat ones, thin ones, the runny-nosed and the pimple-faced too, freckled and wart-covered, toddlers and babies in their mothers' arms, plain ones and pretty ones, tall and gangly or runt-sized. Jesus welcomed them all.

"Hold on, there!" cried the disciples. "Stand back! This is no way to treat the Master! He is in a hurry, and He has no time——"

But Jesus said: "Let the little children come to Me, and forbid them not! For the kingdom of heaven is for such as these."

And tenderly He laid His hands on the head of each and every child there, and prayed, and blessed them all. And not until He had blessed them all separately, did He stride off down the highway, on His way at last.

The apostles followed in silence, shame-faced, their eyes fixed on the ground.

In their minds the words of Jesus echoed over and over again.

"Unless you become as little children, you shall not enter the kingdom of heaven!"

What did it mean, to become as little children? *To be humble,* thought John, *and gentle. To love God with a whole heart, and no thought of reward,* thought James. *To trust Him as a Father, and obey Him as a Father, with happiness, and joy, and no questions asked,* said Peter to himself. *To feel at home with God, and know that He loves you!*

"I wish that I were that tousle-haired boy that Jesus held in His arms," said James to his brother John in a whisper.

"I hope with God's help to be like him," answered John. "The secret of heaven is in the hearts of children, in their eyes and in the smile on their lips. Oh that God will give me the heart of a child again!"

Mary
and
Martha

Three friends Jesus had, aside from His disciples, whom He loved very dearly. There was Martha, and her sister Mary, and their brother Lazarus, who lived in the town called Bethany.

For a long time the four had been good friends. At the very beginning of His public teachings, Jesus had met the gentle, shy Lazarus, and Lazarus had brought Him home for supper one night and introduced Him to his sisters. Bethany was only a few miles from Jerusalem, and from then on, whenever He came near the town, Jesus made it His habit to stay with these friends and visit them. Often He had come to preach in the Bethany synagogue, where Lazarus and Martha and Mary worshiped. In fact, it was in that synagogue that Jesus had told the famous story of the Good Samaritan.

It would be hard to find three people more different than these. Lazarus was a hard-working man, but a quiet one, the kind who listens but seldom speaks, who does his good deeds in secret, and never complains of what others do to him. He liked to garden in his spare time, and to make flowers bloom, and he knew how best to prune trees and train vines. He liked the feel and the smell of growing things.

Mary was a thoughtful and dreaming girl, with a mind that was hungry to learn. People in Bethany used to scold Mary and worry about her because she was not forever worrying about her hair and her skin, or primping like other young ladies. She was neat and clean, they admitted, and pretty in her own way, but why was she forever worrying her head about things that didn't concern her? Better that she would learn to sew a fine seam, or to bake a rich cake, and busy herself at home, instead of mooning over thoughts that were too big for her! And Mary, when she heard them speak, only bent her head and smiled.

Now Martha was just the opposite. Martha was the busiest housewife in Bethany—and the most respected. She scrubbed and swept and dusted and washed and ironed and baked and roasted and basted and tasted and spent her days and most of her nights performing all the duties a woman was expected to perform.

Three people, so different, yet Jesus loved them all, equally, which is of course one of the happiest secrets about the Lord.

One day Jesus came to stop at their home. In the cool shadows of the afternoon He sat in the dooryard, talking with Mary, the thinker and dreamer, who sat listening. And they were talking not of things of this world, but of heaven, and of the ways of the kingdom of God. Mary, her black eyes eagerly on the Master's face, asked many questions. She ached to learn every bit she could about the Way and the Truth of Christian life.

But while they talked, from inside the house came a growing clatter of plates and pots and jugs. It was, somehow, a very noisy kitchen this day—almost as if Martha were deliberately making a racket.

Still Jesus and Mary sat talking.

Suddenly Martha, red-faced, hands dripping wet, breath panting, stomped angrily to the doorway. With that terrible politeness that some people use when they are very cross indeed, she spoke to Mary:

"My!" said Martha. "Isn't it nice and cool out here in the yard! I can feel the coolness now that I'm out of the hot kitchen. You know, Mary, we have a great and wonderful Guest tonight, and we must get supper ready. Here you sit, doing nothing, while I bake and stew over a hot fire! Don't think I wouldn't enjoy sitting out here to chat, but after all —someone must make the meal!"

Mary hung her head, and bit her lip. But before she could reply, Martha turned to Jesus,

"Lord, don't You even care that my sister has left me alone to serve? Speak to her, and tell her to help me!"

Mary hopped to her feet, and a blush crept over her cheeks. But Jesus held out His hand to stop her from going in.

"Martha, Martha," He said gently. "You are careful, and troubled about many things. But one thing is necessary. Mary has chosen the best part, which shall not be taken away from her."

Martha opened her mouth wide, and shut it again with a pop.

Never in her born days had she expected such an answer from the Master!

With a swish of her apron, and a toss of her head, she hurried back to the kitchen, as puzzled and unhappy a woman as ever lived.

"What on earth do you suppose He meant?" she said to herself as she pounded the salt into the stew meat.

"He always said He approved of hard work. Am I to blame for doing my job, for goodness' sake? That Mary is just being plain shiftless and lazy sitting out there talking. You'd think she was a man, not a woman with woman's work to do!"

With a sharp blade Martha sliced the onions, a piece of bread between her teeth to keep the tears away.

"Whoever heard of a girl's using her mind instead of her hands?" Martha asked herself.

There—there was the real question!

For in those days the life of girls and of women was far different than what it is today. Only boys learned to read. Only boys went to school. A girl was meant to work in the house, and forget she ever had a mind!

There were no women writers then, or poets, or painters, or teachers. No women in business in Palestine. Or in politics. Even in their own homes no lady was expected to have any thoughts of her own, except about the children she cared for, and the chores of homemaking.

"Did Jesus mean that homemaking wasn't important?" Martha asked herself as she poked at the coals under the copper kettle.

She shook her head, answering herself. No! Jesus knew, and she knew, that Mary did her share around the house. He knew, and honored, the work of women's hands. He meant only that there was more than that in the world for women!

"You know," said Martha to the hourglass that timed her cooking, "what He said out there in the garden is something completely new! It was as if Jesus were opening a door to all women and all girls—to ones not even born yet! As if He were pointing the way for the years ahead. Someday there will be many girls like Mary in the world!"

Then Martha laughed out loud. "But there will always be plenty like me!" she said. "The world needs us both!"

Then with a flurry and a scurry, Martha bustled back to work, bending over her pots and pans.

When the table was set, and the family gathered, Jesus gave thanks for the food they were about to eat. Tasting, He praised Martha's savory stew, and His eyes saw each detail of her work—her crisp linens, her shining dishes. And a blessing was in each look He gave her.

Across the table Mary met Martha's eyes. And the sisters smiled, for both knew they served Jesus, each in her own way.

Lazarus

Out into the desert beyond the Jordan went Jesus and His disciples, far from the dangers of His enemies in Jerusalem. But Jesus was not hiding, and He did not keep His whereabouts a secret. The crowds who believed in Him found Him, and came to Him even there.

One night as Jesus preached by the light of a campfire a messenger on a donkey clattered across the rocks, weary and out of breath.

"I have come from Bethany, Master," he said. "Your friends, Mary and Martha, have sent me to tell You that Lazarus, their brother, whom You love, is sick!"

As he spoke, Jesus stared into the fire. For a moment He was silent. Then He thanked the messenger and told His disciples to give him food and shelter for the night.

Asked Philip: "Lord, will You go and heal Lazarus?"

Jesus shook His head. "This sickness is not unto death," He said, "but for the glory of God, that the Son of God may be glorified by it."

And that was all Jesus said about the matter.

The disciples peered at each other, and pulled their beards in puzzlement. *That didn't sound like the Master! He would heal any stranger who asked, and believed. Yet now Lazarus, whom He really loved, was sick, and Jesus seemed hardly to care. Strange, indeed!*

Then Thomas' face brightened. "He is afraid to go!" he whispered to the others. "He knows it is dangerous to go so near Jerusalem."

"Ah! Good thing He stays here! Sensible!" they said among themselves. "To go back to Bethany, so near the city, would be like walking into the den of a bear. By now the Temple is so alarmed by Him they are surely planning to kill Him. Maybe kill us too! The Master is right. It is all very sad about Lazarus, of course—we all love Lazarus—but it is much wiser to stay here and be safe!"

How little they understood, these men so close to the heart of Jesus!

Then, suddenly, two days later, Jesus announced that He was going to Bethany.

"Why, Lord?" cried the disciples. "The last time we went near Jerusalem You were nearly stoned to death! Why go back?"

"Lazarus, our friend, sleeps. But I go that I may awake him out of sleep," said Jesus.

"Lord," protested the disciples, "if Lazarus sleeps, he shall do well!"

The smile faded from the lips of Jesus and He spoke to them sternly:

"Lazarus is dead!"

Heartbreaking, mournful news, that! *But how did Jesus know?*, they wondered. *No messenger had come. And if Lazarus were dead, why should Jesus go—and run the risk of being killed Himself?*

Then Jesus said an even stranger thing:

"Lazarus is dead. And I am glad, for your sakes, that I was not there—that you may believe. But let us go to him."

Then up spoke Thomas, whose other name was Didymus, which meant "the twin." Thomas, the hard-headed, the doubter, was certain that if Jesus went to Bethany His enemies would somehow kill Him. And Thomas wheeled on the others of the twelve and snapped:

"Let us go also, that we may die with Him."

And sad and fearful though they were, they agreed with Thomas, all of them, from John to Judas Iscariot. But not one of them could understand why Jesus had not gone before, or why He was going now.

The house of Martha and Mary was crowded with mourners, friends and relatives weeping for Lazarus who was dead. As soon as she heard that Jesus was coming, Martha ran out to meet Him.

"Lord!" cried Martha, as she met Him at the edge of town. "If You had been here my brother would not have died!"

Her thin face was red with grief, and her cheeks quivered, but she bowed her head and said, "But now—also I know—whatever you will ask of God, God will give it to you."

Jesus put His warm, strong hand on her trembling shoulder and whispered: "Your brother shall rise again!"

Martha frowned, not daring to hope. Slowly she said, "I know that he shall rise again—in the resurrection at the last day."

Jesus cupped her chin in His hand, and made her eyes meet His, as He said:

"I am the resurrection and the life. He that believes in Me, although he be dead, shall live. And everyone that lives and believes in Me, shall not die forever. Do you believe this?"

"Yes, Lord!" cried Martha. "I have believed that You are Christ the Son of the living God, Who are come into this world."

The look in His eyes comforted her, and released her. She gathered up her skirts and turning, rushed back to the house and called her sister Mary:

"The Master is come and calls for you."

Mary did not wait. She ran out of the house, down the stony hillside. Everybody in the house followed her, thinking perhaps she was going to the grave to weep. And they did not want her to go alone.

Mary did not care who was following. She wanted only to see Jesus, and when she found Him waiting where Martha had left Him, she fell on her knees at His feet and said as her sister had said:

"Lord, if You had been here, my brother would not have died!" Tears poured down Mary's cheeks, and all those who came with her were weeping too.

But Jesus said simply: "Where have you laid him?"

"Lord, come and see!" said her friends and relatives.

And Jesus wept.

Together they walked into the Bethany hills, and as they went, the people seeing the Master weep whispered:

"Look how much He loved Lazarus!"

"Ah, yes, but——" said one.

"But? But what?"

"He has opened the eyes of a man born blind. Couldn't He have caused this man He loved so much not to die?"

Now they were come to the grave of Lazarus. It was a sepulchre, a tomb like a cave, dug down out of the slant of a rocky hill. And the entrance was closed with a boulder.

Jesus said: "Take away the stone."

But Martha said to Him: "Lord, he has been dead four days. By this time . . ."

Jesus looked at her, and she fell silent. And He said, "Did I not say to you that if you believe, you shall see the glory of God?"

And when He said that, the relatives went to push away the stone. Sweating, gasping, and feeling they were doing a mad thing, they rolled it back. And Jesus, going to the edge of the tomb, looked up at the sky and spoke:

"Father, I give thanks that You have heard Me. And I know that You hear Me always, but because of the people who stand about have I said it—that they may believe You have sent Me."

There was a moment of silence. The spring winds blew sweetly on their faces, and the smell of the tomb was crossed with the odor of wild flowers.

Then Jesus cried in a loud voice:

"Lazarus! Come forth!"

And Lazarus came. Lazarus who had been dead and buried four days, came out of the tomb. He was wrapped in grave cloths, bound, hands and feet, by the white winding sheet, and his face was wrapped around with a napkin. But still, Lazarus came into the light of day, back from death to life.

Jesus said: "Loose him, and let him go."

And Lazarus embraced his sisters, and smiling and laughing and weeping with joy and wonder they knelt before the Master Who had said:

"I am the resurrection—and the life."

The Last Supper

At sundown on Thursday of that week, thirteen men met to celebrate the holy feast of Passover in a great gray hall, an upper room in a house on Mount Zion in Jerusalem.

It was a plain room, heavy-beamed and high ceilinged, furnished only with rattan divans and a long oaken table on which tall candles were burning. The flickering light cast long shadows of the apostles against the unwindowed walls.

During the afternoon the lamb they must eat for the Passover dinner had been prepared in the courts of the Temple as was proper. Soon now they would eat it, when twilight brought the official beginning of the Passover feast.

Now they were all gathered in this room as by a kind of miracle. They had not known where to turn for the holy day, or where to go, until that afternoon the Master had called Peter and John, and said:

"Look, as you go into the city, there shall meet you a man carrying a pitcher of water. Follow him into the house where he enters. And you shall say to the good man of the house: 'The Master says to you, where is the guest chamber, where may eat the Passover feast with My disciples?' And he will show you a large dining room, furnished. There you will make things ready."

Every word of which came true immediately. Now here they were, assembled in that same goodman's upper room, all twelve, waiting for the Master to come.

In spite of all that Jesus had foretold, none of them realized that this was to be their last meal together. It was a Jewish holy day, a holiday, and in spite of all their fears they were eager, and busy talking. And, because they were still a long way from being saints, they began an old argument.

"Which one of us is greater?" they asked. "Which one of us will be the closest to the Master in the glory of the future?"

Once before Jesus had rebuked them for such bickering. This time He answered not in words but in action.

In the midst of their argument He suddenly appeared, wrapped in a long blue cloak, at the doorway. They fell silent like children discovered in a squabble.

Laying aside His cloak, Jesus poured water from a pitcher into a basin. Then He knelt at the foot of His strongest and strangest disciple, Peter.

"Master!" gasped Peter. "Do You wash my feet? No! No! *You must not!*"

Jesus, on His knees, looked up at the great heavy-handed fisherman: "What I do, you know not now—but you shall know hereafter."

Peter's face turned deep red. "You shall never wash my feet!"

The Master's voice was calm: "If I wash you not, you shall have no part with Me."

Then Peter bowed his head and said: "Lord, not only my feet, but also my hands and my head."

Turning next to John, Jesus began to wash the feet of each

of the twelve. Twenty-two feet He washed and dried, and at last He came to Judas Iscariot.

Some in the room had already noticed how strangely Judas was acting that evening. Tonight he seemed sad, and somehow apart from all the others. Pale and glassy-eyed he sat; his crown of stiff red curls and his wavy red beard made his eyes seem blacker and darker than ever, and he spoke not at all, not even when Jesus washed his feet.

Then the Master rose and said: "Know you what I have done to you? You call Me Master and Lord; and you say well, for so I am. If I then being your Lord and Master, have washed your feet, you also ought to wash one another's feet. Amen, amen I say to you: the servant is not greater than his lord. Neither is an apostle greater than He that sent him."

And there was the final answer to the question: Who is greatest in the kingdom of heaven? The one who humbles himself, and puts himself last, as Jesus did.

Then Jesus sat at the table surrounded by the twelve familiar faces.

His arms were opened, His hands lying, palms up, on the snowy cloth. His eyes were lowered and He looked at no one.

To His right sat the pale-faced John, his cheek almost touching the Master's shoulder. And farther to the right was baldheaded Peter, absent-mindedly twiddling a knife between his horny thumbs. Near him, Andrew and Simon Zelotes. To the left were bearded Matthew, and Jude Thaddeus, the oldest man at the Last Supper. Then came curly-haired, black-bearded Thomas, and James the Greater, the tall and powerful brother of John. Next to him was Philip the gentle, and Nathanael Bartholomew, at the end of the table with James the Lesser, Jesus' cousin. And finally, on

the opposite side, as if set apart from all others, sat Judas
Iscariot.

"I have desired to eat this Passover feast with you, before
I suffer," said Jesus. "For I say to you that from this time I
will not eat it, till it be fulfilled in the kingdom of God."

After a long silence He lifted His voice in one of the beloved old psalms of David, and all sang with Him, giving
glory to God. A cup of wine was passed and blessed. Then
each ate of the traditional foods of Passover. To each a por-
tion of the bitter herbs, endive and lettuce, dipped into a
compote of almonds, nuts and figs. As children these men
had learned that the color of those fruits was chosen to remind them of the bricks which once in slavery in Egypt the
Jews had been forced to make without straw. And with the
bitter herbs they ate the ancient bread of misery, the matz-
oth, the flat, nearly tasteless crackers that were all the Jews
had had to eat when they fled from the Pharaohs so long
ago. Then they ate the Passover lamb, roasted and savory.

Then Jesus said sadly:

"Amen, amen I say to you—one of you shall betray Me."

Those sudden shocking words of the Master echoed fright-
eningly in the dining room. This was the first time He had
ever said anything like that. Always He had seemed to trust
them all completely. One of them would *betray* Him? Turn
against Him in secret, sell Him out to His enemies, cause His
death? The idea stunned them. They *loved* Him! How could
they betray Him?

Yet, humbly, their faces tight with sorrow, they asked Jesus
one after another:

"Is it I?"

"Is it I, Lord?"

"Who is it?" shouted Peter, glaring around at them all.

And John, who loved Jesus deeply, whose head even then rested on Jesus' chest, asked: "Lord, who is it?"

"He it is to whom I shall reach bread dipped," Jesus answered. "He that dips his hand with Me in the dish, he shall betray Me."

They were like frozen men, unable to move, as the Master dipped a morsel of bread in the dish of lamb and gravy and then quietly held it out toward Judas.

The voice of Judas, the treasurer, trembled as he croaked: "Is it I, Master?"

"You have said it," answered Jesus. Even then He could not keep the pity from His eyes. "That which you do, do quickly."

Judas took the morsel of bread and gravy, and then fled from the room. The door slammed heavily behind him.

Even then, the disciples did not really understand. True, Judas Iscariot was the least popular among them—but who could believe he would sell his Master's life?

As they looked at the door closing behind Judas, they told themselves that Judas must have simply been sent on an errand. After all, he was in charge of the purse and the money for them all. Perhaps Jesus had sent him off to buy supplies, or on some secret mission to give money to the poor.

And when Judas was gone from the candlelit upper room, Jesus did not mention him again.

Instead He turned their eyes to the most important, most dramatic act of His life—so earthly simple, so heavenly in meaning.

He took bread, and blessed it, and broke it, and gave a piece to each of the eleven. And He said:

"Take you, and eat. This—is My Body."

And they ate.

Then He took the chalice, the cup, and filled it with wine,

and gave thanks to God. And He passed the chalice of wine to the eleven, saying:

"Drink you all of this. For this is My Blood of the new testament, which shall be shed for many unto remission of sins."

And they all drank of it—all except Judas, who had gone, but who was still crouched on the stairway outside listening to the great new mystery—the way in which a man becomes one with God.

And Judas knew that for him it was too late.

This was the time of the real parting between Jesus and those who loved Him in this world, this hour after that first communion.

"Little children," He told them softly, "yet a little while I am with you. You shall seek Me, and as I said to the Jews: 'Where I go, you cannot come,' so I say to you now.

"A new commandment I give to you: That you love one another—as I have loved you, also love one another. By this shall all men know that you are My disciples, if you have love one for another."

But Peter cringed at the idea that Jesus was going away. And Peter said: "Lord, where do You go?"

Jesus answered: "Where I go, you cannot follow Me now. But you shall follow hereafter."

Urgently, lovingly, Peter cried, "Why cannot I follow You now? I will lay down my life—I will die, for You!"

Jesus looked at him, gently, but oh so sadly! "Will you lay down your life for Me? Amen, amen I say to you, Peter, the cock shall not crow, till you deny Me three times!"

Peter roared in protest. *Deny Jesus? Say he did not believe in the Master, did not even know Him? Never!*

"Although I should die together with You, I will *not* deny You!"

Jesus raised His hand for silence, and motioned Peter and the others back to their seats. In a whisper He said:

"Let not your heart be troubled. You believe in God, believe also in Me.

"In My Father's house there are many mansions. If it were not so, I would have told you, because I go to prepare a place for you. And if I shall go, and prepare a place for you, I will come again, and will take you to Myself, that where I am, you also may be.

"And where I go, you know, and the way you know."

Thomas, of the black curls, leaned forward. "Lord, we do *not* know where You go—and how can we know the way?"

And Jesus answered, in words that men have been quoting ever since, for two thousand years:

"I am the way, and the truth, and the life. No man comes to the Father, but by Me. If you had known Me, you would without doubt have known My Father also, and from henceforth you shall know Him, and you have seen Him."

Words burst from Philip: "Lord—show us the Father, and it is enough for us!"

"Have I been so long a time with you," sighed Jesus, "and have you not known Me? Philip, he that sees Me, sees the Father also!"

There! In the simplest of words was the answer for which they had waited so long. Jesus, Son of Mary—Jesus of Nazareth—answered for them now:

"I am in the Father. And the Father is in Me."

He was in Himself God, one with the Father Almighty, the Master of heaven and earth. At last He had told them the full, overpowering truth.

At that candlelit table in the upper room God sat with them now.

"If you shall ask Me anything in My name, that I will do.

"If you love Me, keep My commandments. . . .

"If anyone loves Me, he will keep My word, and My Father will love Him, and We will come to Him, and will make Our abode with him. . . ."

As the apostles fixed their eyes on Him in silence, Jesus made His farewell.

"Peace I leave with you. My peace I give to you. Not as the world gives, do I give to you. Let not your heart be troubled nor let it be afraid. . . .

"If you abide in Me, and My words abide in you, you shall ask whatever you will, and it shall be done unto you. . . .

"This is My commandment, that you love one another, as I have loved you. Greater love than this has no man, that a man lay down his life for his friends."

And as the candles burned low in their stands on the table of the Last Supper, Jesus rose and faced the darkness.

"Arise! Let us go!"

And one by one, they followed Him to Gethsemane.

The Dark Garden

It was well after nine o'clock and quite dark when Judas, ready to betray his Master, came out the back doorway of the house of Annas, and into the alley. There the Temple guards and the Roman soldiers collected by the high priest Caiphas waited. They carried lanterns and torches, clubs and staves, and swords.

Judas turned his back on them, leading them around a corner into a jagged and poisonous-smelling little street. Not a sound was heard, except the shuffling feet of the men, the clank of armor, and the lonely howl of some faraway dog. Zig-zag through the streets they went. Pale in the light of spring stars loomed the Temple, and out through a gate they went, and down the steep hills.

Across the brook Kedron, Judas led them, and up toward the Mount of Olives.

The soldiers began to grumble.

"We have heard strange tales about this Jesus," they said. "They say He has mysterious powers. He can raise men from the dead, and walk on the sea, and feed thousands of people with only a few loaves and fishes. He is a Man to be afraid of!"

"He has never harmed anyone," said Judas.

"Where is He?"

"In a farm yard—a place where oil is pressed out of the olives. Some call it the Garden of Gethsemane," said Judas over his shoulder. "It is really a series of gardens, with walls. He has been there often, but never so late. Any other night He and His followers would be at the house of friends."

"What are they doing in the garden?" growled a wart-lipped soldier.

"I don't know. But there is nothing to fear. No one *could* fear Jesus!"

The thirty silver coins jingled in his bag as Judas sighed heavily and led the long column of men and hissing torches. Presently Judas called softly and lifted his hand, and they halted at a high hedge.

Now most of the party knew where they were. This was the farm yard with the oil press—a dark patch of olive trees, not far from the highroad to Bethany.

A little door-like opening had been cut in the hedge around the olive garden. Judas waved back the guards while he leaned in and peered. With narrowing eyes Judas searched among the gnarled and hunchbacked trees. His long, shrew-ish nose sniffed the soft orchard smell and the damp sweetness of night greenery. His peaked ears caught the deep sound of the wind, soughing and murmuring through those ancient olive boughs.

But where were the other eleven apostles and the Master?
Dimly Judas began to make them out.

Far off, in a different part of the garden, he saw eight dark smudges of shadow under the trees. Those must be some of the apostles! And there, nearer to the hedge, in this part of the Garden, three more forms. That vast hunk of man sprawled on the grass, his head on a rolled-up cloak, was surely Peter, snoring. The slim form there by the pavilion was John, also deep in slumber. And that hulk under the biggest olive tree was James—John's brother, of course. They were all asleep.

But where was Jesus? Judas could not see Him.

Judas would have entered then and brought the guards with him, but he was stopped by the sound of a familiar voice at prayer. He stood listening. Somewhere off in the deeper greenery there, where he remembered a white boulder half buried in the earth, Jesus of Nazareth was on His knees. Judas could hear the suffering voice:

"My Father! If it be possible, let this chalice pass from Me!"

Judas twisted his nose in scorn. "Afraid?" he murmured. "He is afraid! He is praying to be let off—to escape——"

But Jesus was not through with His prayer.

"Nevertheless," prayed Jesus, "not as I will, but as You will!"

Then Judas was startled, because of that prayer in Gethsemane. *The Master wanted not to die—yet if the Father insisted, knowing what was best, then He would obediently take death. What a way to pray!* thought Judas. *Such humbleness could not be right for a man.* Most men prayed to tell God what they wanted, to strike a bargain with God. But not Jesus. Instead of forcing His will, He seemed to try to understand God's will so that He might obey it.

The silence after the prayer was touched by a low, swishing sound as of a trailing robe brushing the grass. Out of the dark and walking by starlight, the white figure of Jesus appeared, moving toward a sleeping disciple. Judas could see

Him clearly now—tall, robed, walking barefoot across the chilly field. Jesus bent over the snoring man.

"Peter! What? Could you not watch one hour with Me? Watch you and pray that you enter not into temptation. The spirit indeed is willing but the flesh is weak . . . Sleep, now, and take rest. It is enough! The hour is come! Look, the Son of Man shall be betrayed into the hands of sinners. Rise up. Let us go. He that will destroy Me is at hand."

Then Jesus reached forward His foot and with the bare toes gently joggled Peter's shoulder. The fisherman grunted, rolled over, then sat up violently.

"It is enough, Peter. The hour has come," Jesus said simply.

Peter scrambled to his feet and bared his knife.

Judas waited for no more. He laid a hard damp hand on the wrist of the leader of the soldiers and whispered:

"Now is the time. Let us go in and take Him. You will know Him sure. He will be the One I will kiss!"

The sound of rough voices and the clank of steel, the sight of the fires, brought all the sleepy disciples to their feet. They blinked at the frightening torch-lit scene, shining with cold brilliance of armor and swords.

Judas strode forward until he stood directly in front of Jesus.

"Hail, Master!"

Jesus moved toward Judas and seized him by the shoulders.

"Friend," said the Master sadly. "Whereto are you come?"

Then the arms of Christ drew Judas to Him, and the disciple kissed the Master on the cheek.

At the signal the Roman soldiers came forward, weapons in hand. But Jesus did not at once let Judas go. He held him tightly, His cheek laid against the tough ringlets, eyes lifted, as if asking a favor of the invisible. Then at last He released him, and as Judas stood back, Jesus the prisoner brought His hands together, and held them out as He approached the Roman captain.

That was more than Peter could bear. His fishing knife, a knife with a blade five inches long, gleamed in his hand. And Peter leaped at the officer. A moment's tussle, a disorderly struggle, and then the voice of Jesus:

"Peter! Peter! Put up your sword. . . . Do you think I cannot ask My Father, and He will give Me at once more than twelve legions of angels? How then shall the Scriptures be fulfilled?—for this is the way it must be done."

A little soldier from the Temple scurried forward with a handful of ropes and began to tie the wrists of Jesus. And seeing that, fear overwhelmed the disciples.

This sudden invasion of men in armor and others with cudgels and staves filled them with fright. The torches blazed and fumed. Voices rose in brawling question. Peter and all the others could take no more. Stampeded, like wild creatures, they scampered off into the night. Leaping the hedges and running as fast as legs could carry them, they left Jesus, the captive, alone.

He had done nothing to save Himself.

And as Judas, skulking in the flickering shadows, watched the Master bound, he remembered the strange, humble words of Christ's prayer:

"Lord, not My will, but Thine, be done."

The Trial

Annas, most powerful man in Israel, sat in his chair of state to await the Prisoner. The door flung open. The captain of the guard stood at attention.

"Lord Annas," he said. "Here as you commanded is the prisoner—Jesus of Nazareth!"

Rough hands shoved Jesus into the room, under the circle of light from the hanging candelabrum.

That first glimpse of Jesus jolted Annas like a blow to the heart. He had heard so much about this trouble-maker, and never before had seen Him. And one question pounded in the old man's mind. *What was there about this tall Man in the white robe and sandals that seemed so different?*

Outwardly He seemed quite ordinary. Like all poor men He wore His hair long, under a white turban. His beard was untrimmed. His clothes were plain. Except for His seamless inner robe of blue, He wore the usual garments.

What was it about Jesus? Annas wondered. Was it in the bright glory of His large calm eyes, set so wide apart? They spoke of God, those eyes—of the nearness and goodness of

God. They were alive with power—and with love! Annas looked into those eyes and shivered. This Jesus—this prisoner with bound hands—was looking at him with *pity* in His gaze!

Annas cleared his throat, and straightened his withered old body. No one could pity him! He would show Jesus how important a person he was in Jerusalem!

"Jesus, You are called a blasphemer!" snapped Annas. "Are You a blasphemer? Do You speak evilly and disrespectfully of God?"

Jesus smiled calmly. "I have spoken openly to the world. I have always taught in the synagogue, and in the Temple, where all the Jews gather. And in secret I have spoken nothing. Why do you ask Me? Ask them who heard Me!"

Annas nodded. "I see. Very well, Jesus of Nazareth. I hold You for trial, immediate trial. The charge is blasphemy. The punishment—death!"

They led Jesus directly to the home of the high priest, Caiphas, next to the Temple. Through the narrow dark deserted streets the soldiers hurried Him. Outside Caiphas' front door they waited for orders.

Around Jesus surged an evil-faced mob, villains of the streets, hired by Caiphas for his own dark purposes. Jesus stood, hands bound, unmoving between His guards, never turning His head. Had He looked left, Jesus might have seen Peter, warming his tough old hands nervously over a coal fire, trying to remain hidden in the crowd. Had He looked to the right, He might have seen the young and distressed face of John. But the Master did not turn His head.

Peter was still warming his hands when a young woman carrying a bucket stopped suddenly before him. The girl's name was Huldah, and she was a servant of Caiphas' house. She studied Peter's face.

"You!" she said. "You were also with Jesus, the Galilean."

"I don't know what you are saying," lied Peter uneasily.

"You *were* with Him," Huldah insisted.

"Woman, I know Him not," said Peter. He moved off, hoping to lose himself in the crowd, fearful that the soldiers might hear the girl, and perhaps arrest him too.

But before he could go two steps another maid joined Huldah, crying: "Surely he is one of them. He is from Galilee. You can tell by his accent."

Then Peter swore: "I do not know this Man you are talking about."

The third lie had just left his lips when over the clamor of voices Peter heard the shrill crowing of a cock. Only a few hours before, at the Last Supper, Jesus had told him that before the cock crowed Peter would deny Him three times! And Peter had vowed he would never deny his Lord.

Peter turned and looked into the eyes of Jesus across the room. And the Lord's eyes were filled not with anger but with loving compassion. Jesus understood how weak men are, even those closest to Him, like Peter, whom He had chosen for such great work.

Jesus loved him still! And Peter wept bitter tears.

The Prisoner was kept waiting outside the Hall of Judgment where the trial would be held.

Inside hundreds of oil-burning torches set in niches in the walls lit the enormous auditorium. By eleven o'clock that Thursday night, most of the seventy judges were already in their places, called there by the high priest Caiphas. Turbaned, barefoot, and cross-legged, they sat on embroidered cushions. Nearby were the scribes, with inkhorns, quills, and parchment, ready to record all that was said. In the back were rows of younger men, who some day would become judges. These men, all of them, made up the Sanhedrin, which was the great Jewish court of law.

Learned men and wise, they took their role as judges seriously. They understood that it was their sacred duty to judge wisely, and mercifully, and honor the truth—and never to convict an innocent man.

The drone and buzz of their voices echoed in the great hall, as the judges asked each other what emergency had led Caiphas to call them at this hour. It was almost midnight! They had all heard of this Jesus, of course, even though very few had ever bothered to go to see Him or hear Him. They thought Him harmless. What crime could He have committed to summon them from their warm beds? They did not know that Annas and Caiphas, whom they trusted, were planning to trick them, to stampede them into condemning the most innocent of men.

Annas, wispy-haired and tiny, took his seat. Caiphas, tall and gorgeous in his official robes, strode forward. The trial could begin. Wheeling toward the great doorway Caiphas called out:

"Jesus of Nazareth, stand forth!"

It was just a few minutes past midnight when Jesus stepped into the courtroom between His two guards.

"Let every man know that Jesus of Nazareth is accused of blasphemy," said Caiphas. "We will prove Him guilty. Let the witnesses be called."

But the witnesses were most unimpressive.

"I heard this Man say: 'I will destroy this Temple that is made with hands, and in three days I will build another not made with hands,'" said the first witness, a tall, gaunt, hungry man.

The second witness was a round little man, a merchant in beans and barley.

"I heard Him say: 'Destroy this Temple, and in three days I will raise it up.'"

On their embroidered cushions the judges grew restless. They trusted and respected Annas and Caiphas. They believed they were exactly what they pretended to be, holy and wise men, representing all good and holy Jews. But something strange was happening here.

Now Jesus had two friends in this court, two men who knew and honored Him. One was Nicodemus, who once had come secretly to Jesus by night, to learn about the kingdom of God. Suddenly Nicodemus rose:

"Lord Caiphas—this is a stupid trial—ridiculous! Your witnesses do not agree. And even if they did, there is nothing they say that means that Jesus should be put to death. I say—put an end to this nonsense, and let us go home—and set Jesus free!"

The other judges nodded their heads.

Then Joseph of Arimathea got to his feet. "Lord Caiphas," he said. "You accuse Jesus of many things—but you cannot prove that He is guilty of any crime. It is already an hour past midnight. It is an insult to the dignity of this court to sit here trying to convict an innocent Man!"

Swiftly Annas whispered in the high priest's ear. Then Caiphas rose, in his blue and golden turban, and his robe embroidered with crimson pomegranates, and faced the court. And his smile was crafty and cruel.

You do not believe Jesus is a blasphemer?, he seemed to say. *He has stayed silent—but He will never fail to answer now! Let Him convict Himself!*

"Jesus of Nazareth," cried Caiphas. "I adjure You by the

Living God, by the Almighty, that You tell us if You be the Christ, the Son of God."

Jesus' reply rang clear and loud: "You say that I am!"

And in the way of speaking of those times, the judges understood that Jesus meant: *Yes!*

Again Caiphas challenged Him: "Jesus of Nazareth, I adjure You by the Sabaoth—the numberless armies of angels—by the gracious and merciful God that You tell us if You are the Christ."

Again the crystal-clear voice: "You have said!"

And in the way of speaking of those days, Jesus was replying simply: *Yes!*

"Jesus of Nazareth, I adjure You by the long-suffering and compassionate God that You tell us if You be the Son of God!"

Then Jesus answered so men of all ages should not doubt: *"I am!"*

Caiphas himself turned pale. It was as if lightning had struck the court. Jesus had needed no witnesses—He had convicted Himself. For who could believe a carpenter from Nazareth was truly the Christ? Not these judges! Like many others, they expected the Messiah to come in glory like an earthly king. They were honestly horrified to hear this poor, barefoot wanderer from a small town call Himself the Son of God. For any mere man to do that was by their law a crime punishable by death.

"He has blasphemed! Behold, now you have heard!" Caiphas cried. Then wheeling to face the judges, he asked in a husky whisper: *"What think you?"*

From most of the scribes and priests and elders came a shout:

"He is guilty! We ourselves have heard it from His own mouth. He is guilty—and must die!"

Instantly Caiphas put them to the vote. One by one the judges must rise, and answer to his name, and vote whether Jesus must die. There were only two No's, from Nicodemus, and from Joseph of Arimathea. For the rest, each one of the seventy voted Yea.

In the midst of the solemn voting a man rushed down the great stairs, straight at Caiphas. In his right hand he held up a bag.

"Judas Iscariot!" cried Caiphas. "What do you here?"

"I declare," cried Judas, "that this Man you have condemned to death is innocent. You promised me you would not harm Him. Here is your money!"

And Judas cast his bag on the floor, and the pieces of silver rang sharply on the stone slabs and scattered, gleaming like little living things in all directions. One rolled to the heel of Annas.

"Judas, get you gone!" cried Caiphas. "Guards!"

"High priest," cried Judas. "I repent of what I have done. I have sinned—and betrayed innocent blood."

In the silence that followed, Judas turned agonized eyes on Jesus. But several judges called to him.

"What is your mistake to us?"

"Look you to it!" answered another.

From the throat of the lost apostle came a broken cry. He rushed up the steps and out of the Hall of Hewn Stones and the crowd parted to let him pass into the deepest darkness of the morning hours. Fleeing, where no man pursued him, Judas rushed into an open field where he found a rope and a tree. And there he hanged himself. . . .

Meanwhile, the voting continued, and soon was finished. The vote was death.

In the dark and early chill of Friday, April 7, Governor

Pontius Pilate was waiting for Annas and Caiphas, and their Prisoner. The air of the house before dawn was damp and cold as a dog's nose. Pilate shivered as suddenly he heard a tantara sounded on a horn.

The Prisoner was at the gate.

Pilate went to the balcony, and took his place on the chair of ivory and bronze. Below him on the steps waited Annas and Caiphas, and Jesus of Nazareth.

The Prisoner's face was blotched and bruised. His beautiful seamless robe was spotted and stained with spit from the mouths of soldiers. His hands, held before Him, were still knotted at the wrists. And behind Him and around Him stood the hired mob, muttering hurlyburly villains paid by Caiphas to frighten Pilate.

Swiftly Caiphas explained the case. This Jesus claimed to be Christ the King. He had been condemned to death by the Sanhedrin. Now the Roman Governor must also sentence Him to death, for the Jews by themselves had no legal powers.

Pilate turned to the accused and suddenly roared: "Are You the King of the Jews?"

Jesus answered calmly: "You say it."

Pilate looked down at Jesus, carefully searching His face. Something in those dark luminous eyes spoke to him, some power, some ray of love. And Pilate knew that unusual as it was, he must speak with Jesus alone. Brusquely he ordered Jesus inside, where none could overhear.

He gave the Prisoner a chair, and leaning forward Pilate asked: "Are You really—the King of the Jews?"

Before Jesus could answer, they were interrupted. A soldier, saluting, brought the governor a letter from his wife, Procula—a strange, perfumed note.

"Have nothing to do with that righteous Man," scrawled

Procula. "I have suffered many things this day, and dreamed a dream because of Him."

Pilate scowled. No woman—not even his wife—could tell him what to do! This was an important case. The Man was charged with wanting to overthrow the Roman Empire itself —with being a traitor, a revolutionary, a would-be king.

Pilate repeated: "Are You the King of the Jews?"

Jesus leaned forward quietly. "My kingdom is not of this world."

"But—have You a kingdom, then? *Are* you a king?"

"You say that I am a king!" smiled Jesus. "To this end was I born, and for this cause I came into the world, that I should bear witness to the truth. Everyone that is of truth hears My voice."

And Pilate, hearing His voice, feeling the presence of some mystery for which he had searched all his life, whispered: "What is truth?" And he read the answer in Jesus' eyes.

Pilate leaped to his feet. "Do You not hear the terrible things they say about You? Do You answer nothing? Don't You know I have the power to crucify You—or to set You free?"

Jesus answered: "You should not have any power against Me unless it were given to you from above. He that delivered Me to you has the greater sin."

Pilate's eyes gleamed. This Man understood! Why He even forgave! And Pilate would do anything for a Man like that! He would try to save Him.

Past the torches of the guards they marched, Pilate and Jesus, to face the high priests and the mocking, jeering crowd. Defiantly, Pilate announced:

"I find no cause in this Man! No evil to condemn Him for. Set Him free!"

The crowd, the men Caiphas had hired to demand Jesus' death, went wild with anger.

"You must not set Him free! He is dangerous—He stirs up the people in Galilee," gasped Caiphas, "and then——"

"In Galilee?" Pilate grinned. Here was a way out for him! "If He is from Galilee I cannot judge Him! You must take Him to Herod, the ruler of Galilee!"

Annas grumbled and Caiphas roared, and his mob roared as he had paid them to do, but it was no use. Pilate closed his gates on them, glad to be rid of the problem of Jesus.

He was not rid of it long.

They took Jesus to Herod, as Pilate had commanded. This Herod, the same who had beheaded John the Baptist, was indeed ruler of Galilee. But this night he was staying in the ancient Jerusalem castle of his family, just opposite the Temple. And this night, too, he was feasting and drinking, more than any man should drink of wine.

Herod was too drunk to understand. He belched and hiccuped and cackled with laughter.

"King of the Jews? That's what He says He is?" giggled the fat, slovenly Herod. "Then dress Him as a king!"

A fine white robe Herod put on Jesus, the robe of a king. But judge Him? Never!

"Take Him back to Pilate!" roared Herod.

And the captive Jesus was led out the gate in the white robe of mockery, the drunken jest of a worthless king against Him who is the King of Kings.

Back again across the city to Pilate's castle they led Jesus. Whatever crimes He had committed were done in Jerusalem—and Pilate could not escape deciding what to do with this Man. Once more the Governor sat facing the high priests, and Jesus, and the evil mob. Once more he tried to save Jesus.

"I have examined Him and find Him innocent. I will chastise Him, yes—but then I shall release Him."

Release Him! A yawp of fury came from the mob. Caiphas turned quickly and spoke two words to a man near him, a hired leader of these cutthroats. And from Caiphas' mouth the words ran to the core of the mob and there rose a sudden piercing cry:

"Crucify Him!"

From one, then from a dozen came the uncouth cry. Soon it was a rhythm and a chant—"Crucify Him! Crucify Him!"

Pilate shuddered. If this crowd were to riot, to attack him, the danger was great. Fear ran through him.

He rose and spoke directly to the people.

In Jerusalem, he reminded them, there was an old custom, that on the Feast of Passover the Governor could set one prisoner free. Now, said Pilate, we have another prisoner, the famous revolutionary leader named Barabbas, a murderer, who surely deserved to die.

"Whom shall I release to you—Barabbas, or Jesus Christ?"

Caiphas signaled. The crowd screamed:

"Away with this Man. Set Barabbas free!"

Arms outstretched, Pilate tried to plead with them, but they drowned out his words, and screamed:

"Crucify Him!"

Pilate raised his hand furiously for silence. "What evil has this Man done?"

Instantly the bitter, well-paid reply:

"Crucify Him!"

Pilate flung himself into the ivory chair. He gave an exhausted growl and made a sign. The guards took Jesus and stripped Him and beat Him with a whip, scourged Him till He barely had strength to stand.

Then they covered His bleeding back again with His own robe. On His head they pressed a crown of thorns, plaited by two idle soldiers of thorns from the hedges. And they led Him back to Pilate.

"Behold," cried Pilate. "I bring Him forth to you that you may know I find no evil in Him."

The crowd stared at the beaten Jesus, face and hands bloody, but standing straight and serene, with even more dignity than before.

"Crucify Him!" screamed the crowd.

And Pilate, defeated, afraid to protest again, screamed back at them: "Take Him, you, and crucify Him, for I find no evil in Him."

Turning, he called for a basin, a golden bowl of water, such as the Jews themselves used to wash away their sins. In front of them all, he, a Roman, washed his hands. And the coward who was afraid to set Jesus free, cried out for all to hear:

"I am innocent of the blood of this just Man."

The long trial was over at last. Jesus was condemned to be crucified, all very legally by Pilate.

And in the shadows of the wall a woman in a dark blue cloak stood weeping.

Mary had seen her Son. She had seen it all.

The Crucifixion

There was no true dawn that Friday, only a pale yellow creeping into the east slowly taking the place of the pale rose of sunrise.

From the guardroom of the castle of Pilate, Jesus descended the broad stairs in the light of the strange new day.

At the bottom of the steps the cross was waiting. It was a crude thing of wood, blackened and smelling of creosote and tar, the centerpiece rounded and large as the mast of a small ship, and the horizontal bar of a long beam split in half and fixed firmly with two bolted iron clamps.

At the soldiers' orders, Jesus knelt in the street. Part of the crossbar was hooked over His shoulder. Then He must stand with the weight of the cross on His back, and carry it Himself to the place of execution. He must drag it through the stinking, festering streets, never to pause, never to catch His breath. He was not alone in His punishment. Two thieves shared His fate, carrying their crosses in the same death march, strange company for the One Who took nothing but gave all.

Then suddenly, in a narrow part of the street, where today there is a broken stone wall, Jesus tottered, swayed, and fell. Weak He was from the scourging, and the cross was heavy, but the soldiers drew Him to His feet again and forced Him on.

Only a few minutes later Jesus saw in the crowd lining the street the face of His mother. Mary was watching there, by a blind alley that was filled with wretched poor children who clung to her skirts. The eyes of mother and Son met, and all the years were in their glances. Then she was lost to His sight as the howling ragged mob closed around Him.

Dizziness came over Him once more. He was about to fall again. A murmur ran through the guards. Someone must help Him, or this Man would never reach the hill of crucifixion. But it was not for soldiers to carry a cross. Nearby stood a man named Simon, a pilgrim from the city of Cyrene in Africa, come to Jerusalem with his two small sons, Rufus and Alexander. Suddenly a guard pointed a finger, snarled an order.

"You there! Carry that Man's cross. Get on with it!"

Simon bent to help Jesus carry His cross, his two little boys following him in tears. He had done no crime. It was an aching nuisance to take such a load. But Simon did not refuse. And because of that half hour's toil, the world has never forgotten him. Simon, a stranger, and Simon alone, helped Jesus, when all His friends had run away.

Now as Simon moved onward with Jesus, the noise of the crowd took a different note. The city was awakening. News of what had happened to Jesus flew from doorstep to upper window and along the domed rooftops. The women heard it first, and they came running to see if it were true.

Through the gate Jesus passed, out into open country, within view of the gloomy hill. There the women of Jerusa-

lem surged into the road, elbowing aside tramps and drunk-
ards and all the savage crew that followed the cross. Un-
afraid, these housewives, daughters, and widows fought their
way to the Master's side, weeping for Him.

Jesus' face took on new strength as He called to these
women:

"Daughters of Jerusalem! Weep not over Me, but weep for

yourselves and for your children." And with panting breath He warned them of the misery and destruction that would come to the city, before long.

Then, exhausted, even with Simon's help, He fell. And for the third time the soldiers drove Him to His feet. The end of their journey was at hand. He had only to carry the cross up that final stretch of steep hill.

Calvary, that hill! Golgotha, the natives called it, meaning the place of the skull.

It was noon as workmen arranged the crosses on the ground.

The three prisoners stood together—Dysmas and Gestas, the two thieves—and Jesus. The soldiers shoved back the crowd and the laborers laid three crosses near the three new holes in the earth.

High noon, and the sun shone brightly on bay trees and laurel, but on the four edges of the world clouds were gathering. Few noticed the dark ring in the lower part of the sky.

The guards stretched Jesus on the cross. They hammered huge pointed spikes through His palms to the crosspiece—then nailed His feet to the main piece. Then they hoisted the cross high, and dumped the base of it into the open hole.

There, at last, Jesus was crucified between two thieves. The three gaunt crosses stood in bleak silhouette against the paling sky.

On the cross over the head of Jesus, at Pilate's orders, they nailed a sign, written in three languages: Latin, Greek, and Aramaic, which was the language spoken in Jerusalem: "Jesus of Nazareth, the King of the Jews!"

On the hill of Calvary the crowd of watchers grew minute by minute. The soldiers were there, and the ruffians, noisy and careless. The women were there, their faces pale with sadness and horror, and beside them the men, their eyes full of question and doubt. If the court, and Pontius Pilate as well, had condemned this Man, who were they to challenge it? They stood silent before the shouts of the soldiers, and they dared not look on His face.

Jesus turning from their faces murmured to the sky:

"Father, forgive them, for they know not what they do."

Forgive them? All? Where were His friends? Where are you, Peter? Where is John, the well-beloved, John who at our Last Supper laid his head on My breast and wept? Where is John now? And Judas! Judas is in the potter's field, after hanging from a tree. Is that what is to be seen so far, far off on the road to Bethlehem, where Mary's Son was born?

And all the others, where are they? Why did you run away, James and Thomas and Bartholomew and all the rest of you? For your lives you ran, scampering off in the dark rows of olive trees in the Garden of Gethsemane, scattering down the road to home. Why did you forsake Me? Because you feared you too would share this fate. You, too, might bleed and die. But the day is almost here when you will have such faith that fear will no longer matter.

"I thirst," said Jesus.

The soldiers grinned. They made Him a drink—a cup of wine mixed with bitter myrrh and gall and bile. He would not drink it. His last cup on earth was the chalice of the communion at the Last Supper.

At the foot of His cross the Roman guards who had nailed Him there threw dice for His robe which was without seam. They had taken all His garments and divided them into four parts—one for each soldier. But that beautiful seamless robe they did not tear. They gambled for it, instead.

While they threw the dice Jesus looked down and saw that He was not alone. Moving slowly through the crowd, ever closer to the cross, were three women—three Marys close at hand. Mary, His mother, stood at the foot of the cross. And Mary, the wife of Cleophas, His mother's sister, knelt beside her. Mary of Magdalen, out of whom He had once cast seven devils, lay prostrate on the earth.

And who was standing beside His blessed mother? John! John, the well-beloved disciple.

Jesus called out:

"Woman, behold your Son!"

Then turning to John, the drops of sweat glistening on His neck and forehead and cheeks, He said:

"Behold your mother!" And from that day on John would be like another son to Mary. But his love was a symbol of a greater service, for Jesus had spoken to mankind, had showed all living the glory of her motherhood.

The sky was darkening, slowly turning from deep violet-blue to black.

And the high priests came to mock Him:

"He saved others. Let Him save Himself if He be Christ. Save Yourself! Come down from the cross!"

Caiphas, standing with Annas, said out of the side of his mouth, "Others He saved. Himself He cannot save. He trusted in God. Let Him now deliver Him!"

But there were some who noticed that as the darkness deepened a small light shone behind His head.

One of the robbers, Gestas, took up the cry and spitting he said: "If You be the Christ, save Yourself—and us!"

But Dysmas, the thief on the right-hand cross, called back to him: "Neither do you fear God, seeing that you are under the same condemnation. And we are justly punished. But this Man has done no evil."

Then turning his head to the Master, Dysmas said with pleading sweetness: "Lord, remember me when You shall come into Your Kingdom."

Jesus opened His eyes, and through the blood and sweat He smiled, and spoke in His old clear, strong voice:

"So be it. I say to you—this day you shall be with Me in Paradise."

The storm was gathering its darkness now. The air was black and murky. There was a low roll of thunder, swelling to roar and crash over the heads of the people. And they began to fear. This was no ordinary storm. This was a brooding, deepening, lightless storm of sinister intensity.

It was close upon three o'clock in the afternoon, when for the fourth time they heard Jesus speak:

"My God, My God, why have You forsaken Me?"

Standing near the cross, Caiphas chuckled hoarsely.

"Hear that, Lord Annas? First He says He is God—then He asks Himself why He has forsaken Himself? That proves He's not God!"

The voice of Annas was low, and sad. "Do you not know your Scriptures, Caiphas? The Twenty-Second Psalm, have you not read it? It begins with those same words. And it tells what happened here today—every bit of it. King David wrote that psalm, predicting exactly this moment."

Jesus let them pour vinegar down His parched throat, vinegar from a sponge for His thirst. Then He spoke again:

"It is consummated."

And even Caiphas knew what that meant. Everything the prophets of the Old Testament had ever said had been fulfilled. Jesus was in truth the Messiah!

Then Jesus took a deep breath and spoke out softly, spoke as Mary remembered He would often speak when He was a boy, falling off to sleep on His bed in Nazareth—softly, and with a tone of surrender and relief:

"Father, into Your hands I commend My spirit."

And bowing His head, He died, about three o'clock in the murky air of Good Friday afternoon, April 7, A.D. 30.

Strange things happened then. The earth trembled and

rocks crashed from the hillsides. Graves burst open. And the veil that hid the altar in the Temple was ripped from top to bottom, although no man's hand had touched it.

Those at the cross who loved Him beat their breasts and sobbed. And the Roman officer who had given the orders for His execution fell on his knees and gasped:

"Indeed this Man *was* the Son of God."

The Resurrection

They buried Jesus that same afternoon.

Mary, His mother, and Mary Cleophas, her sister, and Mary Magdalen, and John, and the two good judges of the Sanhedrin who had voted to free Jesus—Nicodemus and Joseph of Arimathea—were there. They buried Him in a tomb in the garden of Joseph of Arimathea's house, a tomb the judge had built for the day of his own death.

While the women wept, and prayed, the men laid Jesus in the grave. And they sealed the opening of that tomb with a giant white boulder, rolling it into place, firmly closing the tomb. They thought they had closed it forever.

Then, silent, and aching-hearted they went to the upper room, the room where only twenty-four hours before Jesus had shared the Last Supper with His apostles.

They were all there that Friday night—all except Judas. They sat around the oaken table wordlessly staring at the stone walls and the high-beamed ceiling, remembering.

They remembered every moment of the three years they had spent with Him. The way He had called them to follow

Him. The first miracle, the wine at the wedding feast in Cana. The woman at the well in Samaria, and Jacob, the rich man's son who was healed. The Sermon on the Mount, those blessed words. The little daughter of Jairus, and the boy, Seth, with the loaves and fishes. The hour of glory when the Master was transfigured, and the night He walked on the stormy sea. And the day He called Lazarus back from the dead. . . .

Miracles, and the words of truth floated through their minds, the uncounted healings of His hands, the infinite power of love in His eyes.

And remembering, they wept.

Why should it end this way? they whispered. *What are we to do now? We are afraid to go out, afraid we too will be arrested. And Jesus is dead. We have no leader. No one to serve. It is over. Finished!*

The apostles sat in the rain-lashed darkness of that night, lonely, fearful, and discouraged, more than men have ever been since.

Jesus was dead. They could think no further than that. They could not seem to remember the promise He had made to them, so often, so clearly.

He had told them He would die—yes! But He had told them more than that, had told them the greatest, most beautiful secret of all time. How *could* they forget?

Through the darkness of Friday night, and through Saturday and that night too, they stayed in the upper room. This was the Jewish Sabbath, the day when no one could work, or journey far distances, the day to be kept holy for the Lord. But it was not simply because of the Sabbath that they stayed. They were afraid.

Only Mary, His mother, seemed undisturbed. Apart from the others, she prayed day and night and her face was calm.

But the apostles, disconsolate, forlorn—they were a sorry lot.

Meanwhile, in those bleak hours, others were busy in Jerusalem. From the castle of Pontius Pilate soldiers marched, out to the garden of Joseph of Arimathea, out to the sealed tomb.

Caiphas had come to Pilate, Caiphas who remembered though the apostles had forgotten.

"Sire," said High Priest Caiphas to Pilate, "we have remembered that Jesus said while He was still alive: 'After three days, I will rise again.' Will you, therefore, command that His tomb be guarded till the third day—just to be certain this can never happen?"

And Pilate had sent Roman soldiers to the grave, had them test the firmness of the stone, and commanded them to guard the tomb with their lives.

Through the dark watches of Holy Saturday night, eleven men from Galilee, apostles without a Master, and four faithful women, prayed and wondered and wept.

But just before dawn, one person left that room, a woman who loved her Lord, Mary Magdalen. She wrapped her veil and mantle close to her and stepped noiselessly out the door, and sped on tiptoe through the city.

She was the first to reach the tomb.

Breathless she entered Joseph of Arimathea's garden. And what she saw there in the dim light filled her with dread.

The stone had been rolled away. And the tomb—was empty!

Easter morning had dawned at last.

Jesus was risen, risen from the dead. He had died and

death could not hold Him. He had triumphed over death, resurrected He was, risen and shining.

The first Easter—a morning of wonder and of glory, of angels gleaming on the rolled-back stone proclaiming the message:

"He is not here! Christ the Lord is risen!"

And Mary Magdalen, alone in the garden, saw Jesus and talked with Him, saw Him all alive, and smiling, with glory round His face and form, and tenderness in His voice.

Soon all were to see Him, and talk with Him, to eat with Him even, and know Him for their own. Thomas, doubting Thomas, would feel the wounds in Jesus' hands, and be convinced that this indeed was the same Jesus Who had died on the cross.

Forty days He would spend with them in Galilee, forty days of blessing, and final preparation. Then from the Mount of Olives, before their eyes He would ascend into heaven, vanishing into the silver shelter of a cloud.

Soon too, the Holy Ghost would come upon these first Christians in tongues of fire on Pentecost, and then they would go forth into the whole world, as Jesus had commanded, teaching all nations. And the men and women whom they taught, would teach others, and the truth would pass through the years unchanged. From those same apostles to you and to me would come the greatest story ever told, about the greatest life ever lived—the story of Jesus Christ.

But all that was still in the future that first Easter Sunday morning.

Then the apostles knew only one thing: the stone was rolled back. The tomb was empty. And Jesus, Son of Man, Son of God, was risen, returned from the dead.

The words of the angels on that morning of sunburst echoed in their hearts, the never-to-be-forgotten answer to the blackness of Good Friday:

"Christ is risen!"